AQA GCSE

MATHEMATICS
Higher sets
PRACTICE BOOK

Series editor: **Glyn Payne**

Authors: **Greg Byrd, Lynn Byrd**

www.pearsonschools.co.uk

✓ Free online support
✓ Useful weblinks
✓ 24 hour online ordering

0845 630 22 22

Longman

Part of Pearson

Longman is an imprint of Pearson Education Limited, a company incorporated in England and Wales, having its registered office at Edinburgh Gate, Harlow, Essex, CM20 2JE. Registered company number: 872828

www.pearsonschoolsandfecolleges.co.uk

Longman is a registered trademark of Pearson Education Limited

Text © Pearson Education Limited 2010

First published 2010
14 13
10 9 8 7 6 5 4

510.76 AQA
CLL21871
IWK

British Library Cataloguing in Publication Data

A catalogue record for this book is available from the British Library.
ISBN 978 1 408 23277 4

Edited by Alex Sharpe
Designed by Pearson Education Limited
Typeset by Tech-Set Ltd, Gateshead
Original illustrations © Pearson Education Ltd 2010
Illustrated by Tech-Set Ltd
Cover design by Wooden Ark
Cover photo © Getty Images/Aurora
Printed in Malaysia, PJB CTP

Acknowledgements

Every effort has been made to contact copyright holders of material reproduced in this book. Any omissions will be rectified in subsequent printings if notice is given to the publishers.

£7.99

Grades D to A* . . . Grades D to A* . . . Grades D to A* . . . Grades D to A* . . .

III

From 2010 the AQA GCSE Maths specifications have changed. For both Unitised and Linear, the main features of this change are twofold.

Firstly the Assessment Objectives (AOs) have been revised so there is more focus on problem-solving. The new AO2 and AO3 questions will form about half of the questions in the exam. We provide lots of practice in this book, with AO2 and AO3 questions clearly labelled.

Secondly about a quarter of the questions in the exam will test functional maths. This means that they use maths in a real-life situation. Again we provide lots of clearly labelled practice for functional questions.

What does an AO2 question look like?

"**AO2** select and apply mathematical methods in a range of contexts."

An AO2 question will ask you to use a mathematical technique in an unfamiliar way.

> **A** **2** Sandeep says, 'I know that $\frac{1}{9}$ is $0.\dot{1}$, so this means that $\frac{1}{99}$ is $0.0\dot{1}$'
>
> Alisha says, 'You're wrong, $\frac{1}{9}$ is $0.\dot{1}$, so this means that $\frac{1}{90}$ is $0.0\dot{1}$'
>
> **AO2** Who is correct? Show working to prove your answer.

> This just needs you to (a) read and understand the question and (b) form a plan to test the two different claims. Simple!

What does an AO3 question look like?

"**AO3** interpret and analyse problems and generate strategies to solve them."

AO3 questions give you less help. You might have to use a range of mathematical techniques, or solve a multi-step problem without any guidance.

> **A** **3** The diagram shows a radio mast with two guy wires.
>
> Beth is near the foot of the radio mast.
> She measures the angle of elevation from the guy wire at *A* as 62°.
> She walks 30 m away from the mast to another guy wire at *B*.
> The angle of elevation here is 50°.
>
> **AO3** Calculate the length of the guy wire at *B* correct to one decimal place.

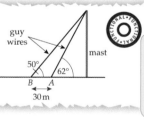

> Here you need to read and analyse the question. Then use your knowledge of trigonometry to solve this problem.

What does a functional question look like?

When you are answering functional questions you should plan your work. Always make sure that you explain how your answer relates to the question.

> **C** **3** A Japanese tourist in London wants to buy a suit in Savile Row.
> The price of the suit is £1250. The exchange rate is £1 = 145 yen.
> a What is the price of the suit in yen?
> A week later the price of the same suit is 171 250 yen.
> b What is the new exchange rate?

> Read the question carefully.

> Think what maths you need and plan the order in which you'll work.

> Follow your plan. Check your calculation. Job done!

How to use this book

This book has all the features you need to achieve the best possible grade in your AQA GCSE Higher exam, **both Unitised and Linear**. Throughout the book you'll find full coverage of Grades D-A*, the new Assessment Objectives and Functional Maths.

At the end of the book you will find a **complete set of Unitised Practice Papers and a complete set for Linear**.

Key points at the start of every chapter – a quick reminder of the main skills you'll need for that chapter, with each skill graded.

Links to the Higher Sets student book in case you need extra help.

Questions which use functional maths are highlighted.

Examiners' hints when you really need them.

All questions graded, with AO2, AO3 and Functional questions clearly indicated.

Every question graded, with AO2 & AO3 clearly highlighted – plenty of opportunities to practise your problem solving skills.

5 Practice Papers at back of book: complete set of Unitised (Units 1-3) and complete set of Linear (Papers 1 & 2)

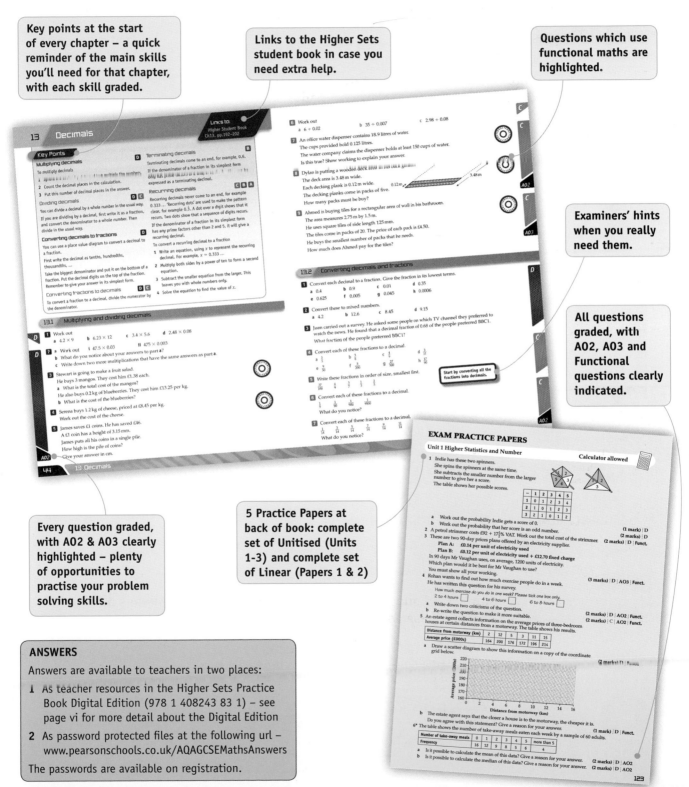

ANSWERS

Answers are available to teachers in two places:

1 As teacher resources in the Higher Sets Practice Book Digital Edition (978 1 408243 83 1) – see page vi for more detail about the Digital Edition

2 As password protected files at the following url – www.pearsonschools.co.uk/AQAGCSEMathsAnswers

The passwords are available on registration.

Grades D to A* ... Grades D to A* ... Grades D to A* ... Grades D to A* ...

v

About the Digital Edition

We have produced a **Digital Edition** of the Higher Practice Book (ISBN 978 1 408243 83 1) for display on an electronic whiteboard or via a VLE. The digital edition is available for purchase separately. It makes use of our unique **ActiveTeach** platform and will integrate with any other ActiveTeach products that you have purchased from the **AQA GCSE Mathematics 2010 series**.

> **Complete flexibility: use the digital edition to display the Practice Book on a whiteboard or through a VLE.**

> **Print out any page required from the bank of PDFs saved on the disc.**

> **Display the answers to any exercise on the whiteboard**

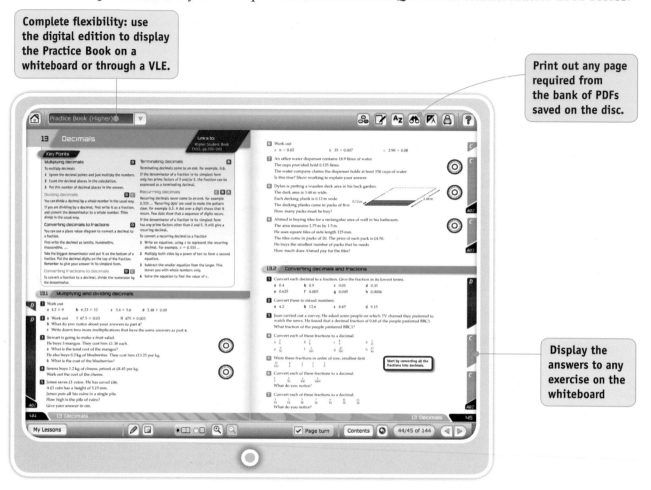

Higher Tier Resources in the AQA GCSE Mathematics 2010 Series

STUDENT BOOK	PRACTICE BOOK	EXTENSION PRACTICE BOOK	TEACHER GUIDE with EDITABLE CD-ROM
D-A* 9781408232781	D-A* 9781408232774	A-A* 9781408240892	D-A* 9781408232798

ACTIVETEACH CD-ROM	PRACTICE BOOK - Digital Edition	EXTENSION PRACTICE BOOK - Digital Edition	ASSESSMENT PACK with EDITABLE CD-ROM - Covering all sets
D-A* 9781408232767	D-A* 9781408243831	A-A* 9781408243800	G-A* 9781408232842

Key Points

Data collection tables [D]

A data collection table or frequency table has three columns: one for listing the items you are going to count, one for tally marks and one to record the frequency of each item.

The data handling cycle [D]

A statistical investigation follows the data handling cycle.

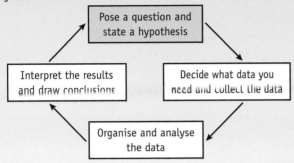

Pose a question and state a hypothesis

Interpret the results and draw conclusions

Decide what data you need and collect the data

Organise and analyse the data

Stating a hypothesis [D]

A hypothesis is a statement that helps to answer a question.

A hypothesis must be written so that the answer is 'true' or 'false'.

Data sources [D]

Primary data is data you collect yourself.

Secondary data is data that has already been collected by someone else.

Types of data [D]

Qualitative data can only be described in words.

Quantitative data can be given numerical values and is either discrete or continuous.

Discrete data can only have certain values.

Continuous data can take any value in a range and can be measured.

Grouped frequency tables for discrete data [D]

Class intervals for grouped data are usually equal.

Grouped frequency tables for continuous data [D]

Continuous data can take values anywhere in a range.

$160 \leqslant h < 170$ means a height from 160 cm up to but not including a height of 170 cm.

Recording data in a two-way table [D]

A two-way table helps you to present related data in a way that makes it easy to answer simple questions.

Questionnaires [C]

A survey collects primary data. One way to collect this data is to use a questionnaire.

A questionnaire is a form that people fill in.

Sampling techniques [C]

The total number of people you *could* ask to take part in a survey is called the population.

The smaller group of people you *do* ask is called a sample.

A representative sample is a sample that will give you a fair and balanced range of people's opinions.

A sample that is not representative of the population will be biased.

Random sampling allows every member of the population an equal chance of being selected.

Stratified sampling [A] [A*]

A stratified sample first divides the population into groups. Then it takes a simple random sample from each group. The number chosen from each group is the same fraction as the sample size is of the population. This is called the sampling fraction.

1.1 The data handling cycle

1 'Old people are better at driving cars than young people.' [D]

   a Give a reason why this is not a good hypothesis.

   b Rewrite the hypothesis to make it easier to test.

2 'Eating sweets makes your teeth fall out.'

   a Give a reason why this is not a good hypothesis.

   b Rewrite the hypothesis to make it easier to test.

D

1 'More DVDs were sold in 2009 than in 2008.'

To test this hypothesis, would you need primary or secondary data?

2 'Barcelona had more rain in 2009 than London.'

To test this hypothesis, how would you find or collect the data?

3 'People living in your street prefer to watch a DVD than go to the cinema.'

To test this hypothesis you would need primary data. Once you have this data, how would you use it?

4 'Adults living near you, with more than two children, buy bigger cars than those with no children.'

  a To test this hypothesis, would you need primary or secondary data?

  b How would you find or collect the data?

  c How would you use the data?

1.3   Types of data

D

1 Use 'the colour of a jumper', and 'the number of students in a class', to explain the difference between quantitative and qualitative data.

2 Use 'the weight of a jumper', and 'the number of students in a class', to explain the difference between discrete and continuous data.

3 Copy this table and put each type of data into the correct section.

The first one has been done for you.

  A   The weight of a hedgehog.

  B   The number of spines on a hedgehog.

  C   The length of a spine on a hedgehog.

  D   The number of fleas on a hedgehog.

  E   The colour of the fleas on a hedgehog.

  F   The weight of the fleas on a hedgehog.

  G   The names of hedgehog rescue centres.

Quantitative discrete	Quantitative continuous	Qualitative
	A	

1.4   Grouped data

D

1 Here are the times taken by some of the entrants in a charity breath-holding competition. The times are given to the nearest second.

56   53   82   59   51   86   81   65   44   52   57

51   40   72   57   45   48   82   47   81   68   42

48   48   57   55   78   52   64   51   71   55   72

  a Put the times into a grouped frequency table using the class intervals $40 \leqslant t < 45$, $45 \leqslant t < 50$ etc., where t represents the time in seconds.

  b How many entrants' times are shown in the table?

  c Which class interval contained the most times?

  d How many of the entrants held their breath for 1 minute or more?

2 A nurse has collected data on the cholesterol levels of overweight patients. These are her results.

6.2	5.1	6.5	8.6	7.4	4.2	9.9	6.5	6.8
8.2	3.2	4.5	9.6	5.9	9.1	8.4	8.0	7.6
5.0	9.6	10.4	8.8	7.5	7.3	9.4	8.3	8.4
5.7	10.9	4.9	7.8	7.9	6.9	9.7	8.9	8.7

a Design a grouped frequency table to illustrate this data. Choose suitable class intervals.

b Any patient with a cholesterol level above 8.5 needs immediate attention. What percentage of these patients need immediate attention?

3 This grouped frequency table shows the distances a cricket ball was thrown at a charity sports event.

Distance, d, (metres)	Frequency
$5 \leq d < 15$	3
$15 \leq d < 25$	12
$25 \leq d < 35$	17
$35 \leq d < 45$	26
$45 \leq d < 55$	47
$55 \leq d < 65$	15
$65 \leq d < 75$	1

a How many times was the cricket ball thrown?

b How many times was the cricket ball thrown less than 45 m?

c How many times was the cricket ball thrown 55 m or more?

d In which class interval were there the most throws?

A02

1.5 Two-way tables

1 This two-way table shows the end-of-season results of a darts team.

	Won	Lost	Drawn	Total
Home	7			
Away		4	6	13
Total			9	28

a Copy the two-way table and fill in the missing numbers.

b How many home games did the team win?

c How many home games did the team play?

d What fraction of all the games played have the team won?

2 This two-way table shows the numbers of doors and windows in each office in an office block.

		Number of doors		
		1	2	3
Number of windows	1	3	1	0
	2	6	12	1
	3	7	10	3
	4	2	8	7

a How many offices have 2 doors and 2 windows?

b How many offices have 2 doors?

c How many offices have 2 windows?

d How many offices are there in the office block?

e What percentage of the offices have 1 door?

3 In a survey carried out by a travel agent, 100 adults were asked where they went for their main holiday last year.

Of the men that were surveyed, 12 said the UK, 9 went to the USA, 8 did not have a holiday and the rest went to mainland Europe.

Of the 45 women that were surveyed, 21 said the UK, 2 did not have a holiday, 16 went to mainland Europe and the rest went to the USA.

a Design a two-way table to show this information.

b Complete the table, showing the totals for men, women and each holiday destination.

c How many people went for their main holiday to mainland Europe?

1.6　Questionnaires

1 Caroline is designing a questionnaire about exercise.

She includes this question in her questionnaire.

Doing plenty of exercise is good for you. Don't you agree?

Yes ☐　　*Agree* ☐　　*Not sure* ☐

a Give **two** reasons why this question is unsuitable.

b Rewrite the question to make it suitable for a questionnaire.

2 Gillian is designing a questionnaire about people's diets.

She includes this question in her questionnaire.

Do you eat sausages?

Yes ☐　　*No* ☐

If yes, how many times on average do you eat sausages each month?

Once or less ☐　　*2–3 times* ☐　　*4–5 times* ☐　　*more than 5 times* ☐

Give two reasons why this is a good question.

3 Oli is carrying out a survey of the students in his school.

He wants to know about the number of packets of crisps that they eat.

One of his questions is

On average, how many packets of crisps do you eat each week?

a Design a response section for Oli's question.

b Write a question that he can use to find out which is the most popular crisp flavour of the students in his school.

4 **a** Design an observation sheet to show how teachers travel to school. It must show data for male and female teachers.

b Make up data for 30 teachers. Show their responses on your observation sheet.

1.7　Sampling

1 A survey on smoking habits was carried out on people standing outside a pub.

Do you think that this will give a representative sample?
Explain your answer.

2 Jiro wants to find out how teachers at his school travel to work.

He asks the teachers that he sees in the car park.
Why might this sample be unrepresentative?

3 Nikki carries out a survey on whether people enjoy cooking or not.

She stands by the fruit and vegetable stall at her local Saturday market.
Give reasons why the sample might not be representative.

1.8 Stratified sampling

1 The table shows the ages of the students in a sports college.

Age (years)	18	19	20	21	22
Number of students	124	112	130	106	28

A sample of 100 students is required.

Calculate the number of students of each age that should be chosen.

2 The table shows the heights of the students in a sports college.

Height, h (cm)	$150 \leqslant h < 160$	$160 \leqslant h < 170$	$170 \leqslant h < 180$	$180 \leqslant h < 190$
Number of students	73	112	133	42

A 10% stratified sample is required.

a Write down the number of students from each category that should be chosen.

b Add up your numbers from part **a**. What do you notice?
Explain why this has happened.

3 The table shows the numbers of men and women in each year group of a university degree course.

Year group	Males	Females	Total
1	25	37	62
2	20	36	56
3	22	31	53
4	13	16	29
Total	80	120	200

The principal wants a stratified sample of 80 students to complete a questionnaire about the university library.

a Calculate the number of men and women from each year group that should be selected for the sample.

b Explain how you could select a random sample of students.

c Add up all your numbers from part **a**. How will you deal with the problem you have now found?

2 Fractions, decimals and percentages

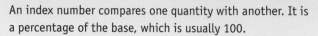

Key Points

Finding a fraction of an amount using a calculator **D**

Most scientific calculators have a fractions key that looks like this $\boxed{a\frac{b}{c}}$ or like this $\boxed{\blacksquare}$.

To find a fraction of an amount, enter the fraction then multiply by the amount.

Writing one quantity as a fraction of another **D**

Make sure both quantities are in the same units, then write the first quantity over the second. Simplify the fraction when possible.

Percentage increase and decrease **D**

Method A

1 Work out the value of the increase (or decrease).

2 Add to (or subtract it from) the original amount.

Method B

1 Add the percentage increase to 100% (or subtract the percentage decrease from 100%).

2 Convert this percentage to a decimal.

3 Multiply it by the original amount.

Writing one quantity as a percentage of another **D** **C**

Write the first quantity as a fraction of the second, then multiply the fraction by 100 to convert it to a percentage.

Index numbers **D** **C**

An index number compares one quantity with another. It is a percentage of the base, which is usually 100.

Calculating with fractions using a calculator **D** **C**

To carry out any calculation involving fractions, enter the fractions on your calculator using the fractions key.

2.1   Fraction of an amount

D

1 Sue runs a guinea pig rescue centre.

On average she feeds each guinea pig $\frac{3}{40}$ of a bag of food per day.

This week there are 43 guinea pigs at the centre.

How many bags of guinea pig food does Sue use this week?

AO2

2 Zina makes a chilli con carne every 5 days.

She uses $\frac{2}{3}$ of a kilogram of mince for each chilli con carne.

How many kilograms of mince does Zina use in April?

D

3 A florist bought 140 white lilies from a market at 79p each.

The florist sold $\frac{4}{7}$ of them for £1.75 each and $\frac{7}{20}$ of them for 99p each.

The rest were not sold and were discarded.

  a How much profit did the florist make?

  b How many lilies were not sold and were discarded?

AO3

4 Tao ate $\frac{2}{7}$ of a pizza and Josef ate $\frac{4}{7}$ of the same pizza.

Josef had 150 grams more pizza than Tao.

What was the weight of pizza that was not eaten?

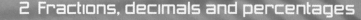

1 Write the first quantity as a fraction of the second.

Cancel your fractions to their lowest terms.

a £3, £36

b 3 m, 72 m

c 9 kg, 12 kg

2 Jim organises an expedition into a rain forest.

As part of the expedition, he finds and records the different types of frogs.

Five of the frogs are new to science, and 22 have been discovered already.

What fraction of the frogs are new to science?

3 Write the first quantity as a fraction of the second. Cancel your fractions to their lowest terms.

a 4 m, 4 km

b 40 g, 6 kg

c £10, £37.50

> **Make sure the units are the same before you start to simplify.**

4 On average, in a rain forest in June, it will rain on 24 days.

For what fraction of June will it not rain?

5 Kieran's aunt gave him some money on his birthday.

He spends £22 and has £18 left.

Kieran says, 'I've still got $\frac{18}{22}$ of my birthday money left.' Is he correct? Explain your answer.

6 Mr Meaner earned £1660 in June.

He spent £850 on household bills and £207.50 paying off his credit card debt.

What fraction of his earnings did Mr Meaner

a spend on household bills

b spend paying off his credit card debt

c have left over?

7 A jeweller has a 2 m length of gold chain.

He uses 42 cm for one type of necklace and 54 cm for another.

The rest of the chain is made into bracelets.

What fraction of the gold chain is made into bracelets?

AO2

1 Use your calculator to work out the following.

Give your answers as mixed numbers.

a $4\frac{1}{5} - 1\frac{2}{7}$

b $3\frac{4}{15} + 5\frac{7}{8}$

c $1\frac{3}{7} - 2\frac{7}{8} + 3\frac{2}{11}$

2 Which calculation gives the smallest answer?

A $32 \times \frac{3}{8}$ B $180 \times \frac{5}{78}$ C $2\frac{4}{5} \times 4\frac{2}{5}$

3 On Saturday, Alice spent $\frac{2}{3}$ of her birthday money.

On Tuesday, she spent $\frac{1}{5}$ of what she had left.

What fraction of her birthday money has Alice not spent?

4 A school has a total of 3200 seats. Each seat is $\frac{13}{20}$ m wide.

If all 3200 seats were placed next to each other in a line, how long would this line be?

Give your answer in

a   metres   b   kilometres   c   miles.

$$\boxed{1 \text{ km} = \tfrac{5}{8} \text{ mile}}$$

5 A full bathtub holds 126 litres of water.

Water pours from a tap at a rate of $2\frac{1}{4}$ litres every 10 seconds.

At this rate, how long does it take to fill the bathtub? Give your answer in minutes and seconds.

6 Every month, Ashur saves $\frac{2}{15}$ of his monthly wage.

How many months will it take Ashur to save three times his monthly wage?

7 Caitlin adds four identical mixed numbers to give $7\frac{3}{5}$.

What are the four numbers?

8 40p is a quarter of two ninths of a sum of money.

What is the total sum of money?

2.4   One quantity as a percentage of another

1 Purdey has 25 DVDs.

She lends three of them to her friend.

What percentage of her DVDs does Purdey lend?

2 Yasuo buys a 1 litre bottle of water.

He drinks 125 ml of the water. What percentage of the water does he drink?

3 Adam swims 80 lengths of a swimming pool every night.

So far tonight he has swum 26 lengths. What percentage of his 80 lengths has he still to swim?

4 Jason gets 34 questions out of 40 correct in a geography test.

What percentage of the test does he get wrong?

5 An athletics club has 127 members.

Women	Men	Girls	Boys
41	23	34	29

What percentage of the members are

a   women   b   male?

Give your answers correct to one decimal place.

6 Last year, Polly earned £27 000.

This year she earns £29 500. What is the percentage increase in Polly's earnings?

Give your answer to one decimal place.

7 Mr Ree buys an old house for £124 950.

He spends £28 150 on improvements and then sells it for £199 500.

What is his percentage profit?

Give your answer to one decimal place.

8 A market stallholder buys 50 melons for 48p each.

She sells 27 for £1.29 in the morning and 16 for 49p in the afternoon.

The rest are not sold and are discarded.

Work out the market stallholder's percentage profit.

Give your answer to one decimal place.

9 Matt has been on a diet for the last nine months.

He has lost 16.4 kg. He now weighs 73.7 kg.

What percentage of his starting weight did Matt lose?

Give your answer to one decimal place.

2.5 Percentage increase and decrease

1 In a sale, the manager of a store reduces the price of a TV by 40%.
Before the sale, the price of the TV was £699.
How much is the TV in the sale?

2 Jeff used to earn £360 a week. He has had a 5% pay rise.
How much does he now earn?

3 The price of a graphic display calculator is £38 plus VAT at 17.5%.
What is the total price of the calculator?

4 Brendan bought a new car for £14 775.

The value of the car went down by 17% in the first year and another 15% in the second year.

How much is the car worth at the end of the second year?

Give your answer to the nearest hundred pounds.

> Do not decrease the value by 32%.

5 Geoff's new puppy weighs 8 kg.

The vet said the puppy should increase its weight by about 10% a week.

How much should the puppy weigh after 4 weeks?

6 Harry bought some shares in a company for £1000.

In the first year, the value of the shares fell by 45%.

In the second year, the value of the shares rose by 20%.

How much are the shares worth after the second year?

7 Dave needs to buy a van for his building company.

The van's price is £8000 + VAT at 17.5%.

Dave buys the van on credit. He pays a deposit of 22.5% and then 48 monthly payments of £165. How much more does Dave pay by buying the van on credit?

D

1 In December 2004, the total amount of money spent in shops using credit cards was £26.2 billion.

The table shows the price index of December credit card spending for the years 2002 to 2006, using 2004 as the base year.

Year	2002	2003	2004	2005	2006
Index	75	87	100	109	118
Price			£26.2 billion		

An index of 75 means that the value was 25% lower than in the base year. An index of 109 means that the value has gone up by 9%.

Work out the December credit card spending from 2002 to 2006.

Give your answers correct to one decimal place.

2 This year, the index for the price of milk, compared with 2004 as a base, is 129.

a Has the price of milk gone up or down?

b By what percentage has the price of the milk changed?

3 The retail prices index was introduced in January 1987.

It was given a base number of 100.

Ten years earlier, in January 1977, the index number would have been 43.7.

In January 1987, the 'standard weekly shopping basket' cost £38.50.

How much did the same 'standard weekly shopping basket' cost in January 1977?

C

AO2

4 A factory that makes hand-built cars produced 128 cars in 2008.

This represented an index of 160, using 2000 as the base year with an index of 100.

How many cars did the factory make in 2000?

C

5 The graph shows the exchange rates for the euro (€) and the pound (£) from July 2008 to June 2009.

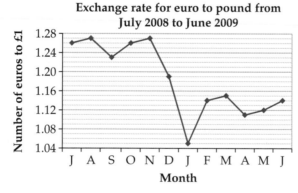

Exchange rate for euro to pound from July 2008 to June 2009

AO3

a What was the exchange rate in November 2008?

b Using July 2008 as the base of 100, work out the index for January 2009.

Key Points

Stem-and-leaf diagrams   D

Stem-and-leaf diagrams can be used to organise discrete data so that analysis is easier. The data is grouped and ordered according to size, from smallest to largest. A key is needed to explain the numbers in the diagram.

Frequency diagrams for continuous data   D

Continuous data can be represented by a frequency diagram. A frequency diagram is similar to a bar chart except that it has no gaps between the bars.

Scatter diagrams and correlation   D   C

Scatter diagrams are used to compare two sets of data. They show whether or not there is a connection or relationship, called a correlation, between the two quantities plotted.

On a scatter diagram, a line of best fit is a straight line that passes through the data with an approximately equal number of points on either side of the line and most points close to the line.

If a line of best fit can be drawn, then there is some form of linear correlation between the two sets of data.

Frequency polygons   C

A frequency polygon shows patterns or trends in the data. When drawing a frequency polygon, the mid-point of each class interval is plotted against the frequency.

Histograms   A   A*

A histogram is a diagram that represents continuous data.

For a histogram,

- there are no gaps between the bars because the data is continuous
- the bars can be different widths, to represent different class widths or class intervals
- the horizontal axis must be on a continuous scale
- the vertical axis represents the frequency density where

$$\text{frequency density} = \frac{\text{frequency}}{\text{class width}}.$$

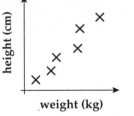

Positive correlation

Negative correlation

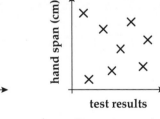

No (linear) correlation

3.1   Stem-and-leaf diagrams

1 The teachers in a school were asked how many years they had been teaching.   D

Here are their answers to the nearest year.

2	10	1	20	21	13	30	7
18	12	17	12	5	16	20	5
23	11	21	3	32	11	8	35
12	06	22	29	6	18	3	7
25	5	15	29	9	15	32	21

a How many teachers are in the school?

b Draw a stem-and-leaf diagram for this data.

c How many of the teachers had been teaching for more than 30 years?

2 Sandeep kept a record of the distances, in km, he ran in the evenings during June.
Here are his results, to the nearest 0.1 km.

6.7 9.2 6.9 8.1 5.9 9.8

7.0 9.5 5.5 8.1 6.7 7.5

8.0 6.2 7.5 7.8 9.5 6.5

a On how many evenings did Sandeep go for a run in June?

b Draw a stem-and-leaf diagram for this data.

c On how many of these evenings did Sandeep run less than 8 km?

3.2 Scatter diagrams

1 Mr Scrivener recorded the PE and maths exam results for the 12 students in both his PE class and his maths class. The table shows his results.

PE mark	22	58	67	32	75	44	88	18	23	52	72	95
Maths mark	68	43	38	64	28	52	86	72	28	55	25	14

a Plot this information on a scatter diagram.

b Describe the relationship between the students' PE marks and their maths marks.

c On your scatter diagram, circle the two plots for the students whose marks don't fit the general trend. What can you say about these two students?

2 The table shows the mean temperature in August in 10 cities north of the equator. It also shows the latitude of the cities.

City	Mean temperature in August (°C)	Latitude (°N)
Barcelona	24	41
Helsinki	16	60
Athens	28	37
London	19	51
Tucson	26	32
Hong Kong	28	23
Vorkuta	10	67
Bangkok	32	14
Kabul	24	34
Edinburgh	14	56

> The latitude is the number of degrees a place is north (or south) of the equator.

a Plot this information on a scatter diagram. Plot the latitude along the x-axis (horizontal) and the temperature along the y-axis (vertical).

b Describe the correlation between the latitude of a city and its mean temperature in August.

c Draw a line of best fit on your scatter diagram.

d Use your line of best fit to estimate
  i the mean temperature in August of a city with latitude 12 degrees north
  ii the latitude of a city with mean temperature in August of 20°C.

e Would it be sensible to use the line of best fit to estimate the mean temperature in August of a city with latitude 72 degrees north?
Give a reason for your answer.

1 The daily rainfall, in mm, was recorded in Aberdeen over a period of 60 days. The table shows the results.

Draw a frequency diagram to show this data.

Rainfall, r (mm)	Frequency
$2.0 \leqslant r < 2.2$	8
$2.2 \leqslant r < 2.4$	11
$2.4 \leqslant r < 2.6$	6
$2.6 \leqslant r < 2.8$	19
$2.8 \leqslant r < 3.0$	16

D

2 The average daily temperature, in °C, was recorded in Aberdeen over the same period of 60 days as Q1. The table shows the results.

a Draw a frequency diagram to show this data.

b Look at the frequency diagrams you have drawn in Q1 and Q2a.

Do you think that these 60 days are a good time of year to visit Aberdeen?

Give reasons for your answer.

Temperature, t (°C)	Frequency
$3 \leqslant t < 4$	21
$4 \leqslant t < 5$	14
$5 \leqslant t < 6$	13
$6 \leqslant t < 7$	7
$7 \leqslant t < 8$	5

D

AO2

1 The frequency table shows the average minimum temperatures, in °C, in Copenhagen over a 20-week period.

Temperature, t (°C)	Frequency	Mid-point
$10 \leqslant t < 12$	4	
$12 \leqslant t < 14$	8	
$14 \leqslant t < 16$	6	
$16 \leqslant t < 18$	2	

a Copy and complete the table.

b Draw a frequency polygon of this data.

C

2 The frequency table shows the average maximum temperatures, in °C, in Copenhagen over the same 20-week period as Q1.

a Copy and complete the table.

b Draw a frequency polygon of this data.

c On how many days was the temperature below 22°C?

Temperature, t (°C)	Frequency	Mid-point
$16 \leqslant t < 19$	2	
$19 \leqslant t < 22$	7	
$22 \leqslant t < 25$	7	
$25 \leqslant t < 28$	4	

3 The two frequency polygons show the age distributions of people at a rock concert and a classical music concert.

Which polygon do you think represents the age distribution of the people at a rock concert?

Give reasons for your answer.

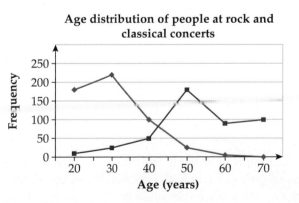

Age distribution of people at rock and classical concerts

C

AO3

A

1 The frequency table show the salary structure of the 25 employees in a company.

Salary, s (£)	Frequency	Class width	Frequency density
$5000 \leqslant s < 15\,000$	3		
$15\,000 \leqslant s < 20\,000$	6		
$20\,000 \leqslant s < 25\,000$	9		
$25\,000 \leqslant s < 30\,000$	5		
$30\,000 \leqslant s < 50\,000$	2		

 a Copy and complete the table.

 b Draw a histogram to illustrate this data.

A*

2 The histogram shows information about the ages of the members of a gym.

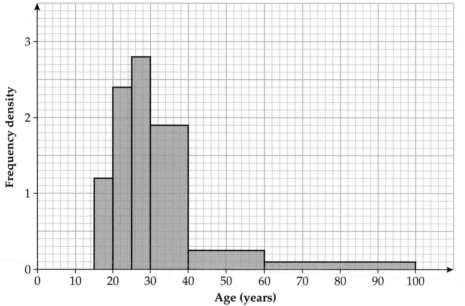

Age of members of a gym

 a Work out the number of members of the gym.

 b Estimate the number of members over the age of 50.

 c Harry says, 'Less than a quarter of the members of the gym are under 25 years old.' Is he correct? Explain your answer.

AO2

Key Points

Averages and range   **D**

The mean is the most commonly used average.

$$\text{mean} = \frac{\text{sum of all the data values}}{\text{number of data values}}$$

The median is the middle value when the data is written in order.

With n data values, median $= \left(\dfrac{n+1}{2}\right)$th value.

The mode, or modal value, of a set of data is the number or item that occurs most often.

The range of a set of data is the difference between the largest value and the smallest value.

range = largest value − smallest value

Range, median and mode from a grouped frequency table   **D** **C**

The class interval with the highest frequency is called the modal class.

You can estimate the range using the formula

estimated range = highest value of largest class interval
           − lowest value of smallest class interval

With n data values, the median is the $\left(\dfrac{n+1}{2}\right)$th value data value.

You can use this formula to work out which class interval contains the median.

Estimating the mean from a grouped frequency table   **C**

You can estimate the mean by assuming that every data value lies exactly in the middle of a class interval. You need to work out the mid-point of each class interval.

mid-point
$= \dfrac{\text{minimum class interval value} + \text{maximum class interval value}}{2}$

estimate of mean
$= \dfrac{\text{total of 'mid-point} \times \text{frequency' column}}{\text{total frequency}}$

Appropriate averages   **A**

The mode is the only average you can use for qualitative data. The mode tells you which data value is most likely to occur.

The median tells you the middle value. Half the data values are greater than the median and half are less than the median.

The mean is the only average that takes every value into account. The mean can be affected by very high or very low values. These values are called extreme values.

4.1   Calculating the mean, median, mode and range from a frequency table

1 A football team recorded the number of goals they scored each match during one season.

The table shows their results.

Number of goals	Frequency
0	7
1	12
2	8
3	4
4	4
5	2

a Work out the range of this data.

b Write down the mode of this data.

c Work out the median of this data.

d Calculate the mean number of goals per match. Give your answer to one decimal place.

    D

2 A hockey team recorded the number of goals they scored each league match during one season.

The table shows their results.

a Work out the range of this data.

b Write down the mode of this data.

c Work out the median of this data.

Number of goals	Frequency
0	0
1	2
2	17
3	4
4	3
5	2

d Calculate the mean number of goals per match.

The table does not include the one friendly match that the hockey team played.

In this match they scored 4 goals.

e If this data were added to the table, how would it affect the mean?

    D

    A02

C **3** An advertising company did a survey on the numbers of times people visited the 'Chirrup' website last week, and their ages. The table shows their results.

a How many 15–19 year olds took part in the survey?

b How many visits were made in total by people in the 15–19 age range?

c Calculate the mean number of visits per person in the 15–19 age range.

d The advertising company wants to target the age range with the highest mean number of visits. Which age range should they target?

AO2

	Frequency			
	Age (years)			
Number of visits	10–14	15–19	20–29	30–49
0	3	5	12	93
1	5	14	8	12
2	4	19	3	4
3	12	17	0	0
4	17	17	0	3
5	2	8	1	0
6	3	2	0	0

4.2   Calculating the range, median and mode from a grouped frequency table

D **1** A driving simulator tests driver reaction times to a child stepping into the road.

The table shows the reaction times of 120 drivers.

C

a Write down the modal class.

b Estimate the range of this data.

c Which class interval contains the median?

Reaction time, t (seconds)	Frequency
$0.2 \leqslant t < 0.3$	27
$0.3 \leqslant t < 0.4$	38
$0.4 \leqslant t < 0.5$	42
$0.5 \leqslant t < 0.6$	9
$0.6 \leqslant t < 0.7$	4

D **2** The grouped frequency table shows the heights of the students in a sports studies class.

a Write down the modal class.

b Estimate the range of this data.

c Which class interval contains the median?

d Three new students join the class.

Their heights are all within the $150 \leqslant h < 160$ interval.

What effect will this new data have on

  i the modal class

  ii the estimated range

  iii the class containing the median?

Height, h (cm)	Frequency
$140 \leqslant h < 150$	2
$150 \leqslant h < 160$	4
$160 \leqslant h < 170$	7
$170 \leqslant h < 180$	14
$180 \leqslant h < 190$	1

C

e How might the class tutor explain that the exact mean height cannot be found from the grouped frequency table?

AO2

4.3   Estimating the mean from a grouped frequency table

C **1** The grouped frequency table shows the heights of the students in a sports studies class.

Height, h (cm)	Frequency	Mid-point	Mid-point × frequency
$140 \leqslant h < 150$	2	145	145 × 2 = 290
$150 \leqslant h < 160$	4		
$160 \leqslant h < 170$	7		
$170 \leqslant h < 180$	14		
$180 \leqslant h < 190$	1		
Total			

a Copy and complete the table to work out an estimate of the total height of all the students.

b Calculate an estimate of the mean height of the students, correct to one decimal place.

2 A driving simulator tests driver reaction times to a child stepping into the road.

The tables show the reaction times of 120 drivers before and after a 30 minute rest.

a Calculate an estimate of the mean reaction time of the drivers after they had a rest.

b Write down the class interval which contains the modal reaction time after the drivers had a rest.

c Jack said, 'The average reaction times before and after resting are about the same. Resting does not affect the reaction times.'

Do you agree with Jack's statement?
Give evidence to support your answer.

Before rest	
Reaction time, t (seconds)	Frequency
$0.2 \leqslant t < 0.3$	7
$0.3 \leqslant t < 0.4$	48
$0.4 \leqslant t < 0.5$	21
$0.5 \leqslant t < 0.6$	31
$0.6 \leqslant t < 0.7$	5
$0.7 \leqslant t < 0.8$	8

After rest	
Reaction time, t (seconds)	Frequency
$0.2 \leqslant t < 0.3$	29
$0.3 \leqslant t < 0.4$	38
$0.4 \leqslant t < 0.5$	42
$0.5 \leqslant t < 0.6$	9
$0.6 \leqslant t < 0.7$	2

C

AO2

4.4   Which average?

1 Nigel asked 12 people how many books they read last year. Here are his results.

36   6   100   6   84   8   50   9   6   48   11   8

In his conclusion, Nigel wrote, 'The average person read about six books last year.'

a Calculate the mean, median and mode for this data.

b Which average has Nigel used for his conclusion?

c Do you agree with Nigel's conclusion? Give reasons for your answer.

d Choose an appropriate average and write your own conclusion for Nigel's data.

2 For each investigation, choose the most suitable average. Give reasons for your answers.

a Finding the wage of an average 27-year-old teacher.

b Identifying the most common make of training shoe.

c Comparing the average weights of two litters of kittens.

3 Charlotte was investigating the annual salaries of workers at a newspaper publisher.
Here is the information she found.

> Editor £120 000
> Chief journalist £95 000
> Journalists £52 000, £54 000, £42 000, £45 000
> Office workers £22 000, £18 000

a Calculate the mean annual salary.

b Is the mean a good representation of the average annual salary?

c Calculate the median annual salary.

The newspaper employs an extra office worker.

d What effect will this have on
   i the mean annual salary
   ii the median annual salary?

e Write a conclusion about how the arrival of the new office worker has affected the average annual salary.

A

A

AO2

Links to:
Higher Student Book
Ch5, pp.70–90

Key Points

Mutually exclusive events   **D**

Mutually exclusive events cannot happen at the same time.

$$P(A \text{ or } B) = P(A) + P(B)$$

The number of times an event is likely to happen   **D**

expected frequency =
       probability of event happening × number of trials

Calculating relative frequency   **C**

Relative frequency is also known as experimental or estimated probability.

$$\text{relative frequency} = \frac{\text{number of successful trials}}{\text{total number of trials}}$$

Independent events   **C**

Two events are independent if the outcome of one does not affect the outcome of the other.

$$P(A \text{ and } B) = P(A) \times P(B)$$

Drawing tree diagrams   **B** **A** **A***

The probability of each outcome is written on the branch of the tree, for example

To calculate the probability of combined outcomes, multiply the probabilities, for example
$P(H \text{ and } H) = \frac{1}{2} \times \frac{1}{2} = \frac{1}{4}$.

Conditional probability   **A***

When one event affects the outcome of a second event, the probability of the second event is conditional on (or dependent on) the outcome of the first.

5.1   Mutually exclusive events

D

1   A box contains 20 biscuits.

6 of the biscuits are plain, 6 are choc chip, 5 have caramel centres and 3 are ginger biscuits.

One biscuit is taken from the box at random. What is the probability that the biscuit

   a   has a caramel centre or is choc chip

   b   has a caramel centre or is a ginger biscuit

   c   has a caramel centre or is plain

   d   does not have a caramel centre and is not plain

   e   is not a ginger biscuit or plain or have a caramel centre?

2   Work out the probability of rolling a 1 or a 2 or a 3 with a fair 6-sided dice.

3   A box contains jelly beans with four flavours. One is taken at random.
The table shows the probability of taking each flavour.

   a   What is the probability that the jelly bean is banana or mango flavoured?

   b   What is the probability that the jelly bean is fig flavoured?

Flavour	Probability
banana	0.18
fig	
mango	0.24
pineapple	0.45

D

4   A bag contains sweets.

One sweet is taken from the bag at random.

The table shows the probability of taking each type of sweet.

There are five times as many gobstoppers as sherbet bombs.

A02   What is the probability that the sweet is a sherbet bomb?

Sweet	Probability
humbug	0.27
red rock	0.43
gobstopper	
sherbet bomb	

5 Mick puts 9 HB pencils into a pencil case.

Nora puts 11 2H pencils into the same pencil case.

Ulrika puts some 2B pencils into the pencil case.

The probability of taking a 2B pencil from the pencil case at random is $\frac{1}{5}$.

How many 2B pencils did Ulrika put in the bag?

5.2   Expectation

1 This fair spinner is spun 80 times.

How many times would you expect it to land on

a the number 6

b a number less than 6?

2 Zoe has this 10-sided spinner.

She spins it and notes the number she gets.

She does this 200 times. How many times would you expect her to get

a a 5

b an even number

c a square number

d a prime number?

3 Shaun has a bag containing 3 red, 4 orange, 4 green and 4 silver marker pens.

He selects one marker pen at random from the bag, then replaces it. He does this 90 times.

How many times would you expect him to select a green marker pen?

4 This table shows the probability of selecting coins from a bag.

Coin	£2	£1	50p	10p	5p
Probability	0.19	0.17	0.29	?	?

The probability of selecting a 10p coin is twice the probability of selecting a 5p coin.

Eva selects one coin at random from the bag, then replaces it.
She does this 300 times.

How many times would you expect her to select a 10p coin?

5 At a charity event, Becky runs a 'Wheel of fortune' game.

She charges 50p to spin the wheel.

The wheel is equally likely to stop on any number.

If the wheel stops on a square number she gives a prize of £2.

In total, 200 people play the game.

How much money would you expect Becky to make for the charity?

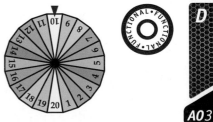

5.3   Relative frequency

1 Twenty-eight Year 8 students were asked if they spent more than £20 on a haircut. Seven answered, 'Yes.'

a What is the relative frequency of 'Yes' answers?

There are 220 students in Year 8.

b How many of these do you estimate will have spent more than £20 on a haircut?

2 Rob rolls a 10-sided dice, numbered 1 to 10. He keeps a tally of how many 1s he rolls. The table shows his results.

Number of rolls	20	50	100	200	500	1000
Number of 1s	2	6	13	28	75	170
Relative frequency						

  a Work out the relative frequency for the number of 1s at each stage of the experiment.

  b Work out the theoretical probability of rolling a 1 on a fair 10-sided dice.

  c Do you think Rob's dice is fair? Explain your answer.

3 Jess has a four-sided dice labelled 1, 2, 3 and 4. She rolls the dice 40 times. Here are her results.

3 4 4 2 1 4 1 1 3 4 4 3 2 2 2 1 1 1 2 1
1 1 3 4 1 3 2 2 3 4 1 2 1 2 1 3 1 4 4 1

  a Copy and complete the relative frequency table.

Number	1	2	3	4
Relative frequency				

  b Jess thinks that the dice is biased. Write down the number you think the dice is biased towards. Explain your answer.

  c What could Jess do to make her results more reliable?

5.4   Independent events

1 A fair 6-sided dice is rolled twice.

  a What is the probability of getting a 1 and then a 3?

  b What is the probability of getting two 4s?

2 Beth has a fair 20-sided dice. It has two of each number from 1 to 10 on its faces.

Beth rolls the dice twice.

  a What is the probability of getting a 5 and then an 8?

  b Beth decides to add the two numbers she rolls to give a score between 2 and 20.

    What is the probability of scoring 19?

3 Bag X contains 3 red and 5 green chillies.

Bag Y contains 4 red and 6 green chillies.

Hazel takes one chilli at random from each bag.
What is the probability that both chillies are

  a red

  b green?

4 Ernst has a fair four-sided dice and a fair spinner numbered 1 to 5.

He rolls the dice and spins the spinner at the same time.

He multiplies the number on the dice and the number on the spinner to give the score.

What is the probability that the score is

  a 9

  b 12

  c greater than 12?

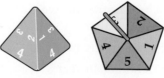

5 Ben rolls a fair dice numbered 1 to 10.

Jerry rolls a fair spinner numbered from 1 to 3. Work out the probability that

a they both get a 3

b they both obtain an odd number

c the total of their scores is 3

d Ben's score is twice Jerry's score

e Jerry's score is greater than Ben's score.

5.5   Tree diagrams

1 Tamsin has a bag containing 2 silver tickets and 5 gold tickets.

She takes a ticket at random from the bag, records the colour then puts it back in the bag.

She then takes a second ticket from the bag.

a Copy and complete the tree diagram to show all the possible outcomes and their probabilities.

b Work out the probability that Tamsin takes
  i 2 silver tickets
  ii 2 gold tickets
  iii a silver then a gold ticket
  iv a gold then a silver ticket.

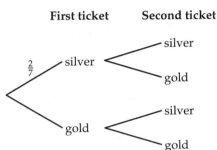

2 Jet, Shen and Tani all go to the same school.

The probability that Jet forgets his homework is 0.1.

The probability that Shen forgets his homework is 0.2.

The probability that Tani forgets his homework is 0.5.

a Draw a tree diagram to show all the possible outcomes.

b On any day, what is the probability that
  i all 3 forget their homework
  ii all 3 remember their homework
  iii Jet forgets his homework but Shen and Tani don't
  iv at least one of them forgets his homework?

3 Polly, Holly and Lily each take 3 horse riding exams: theory, practical and teaching.

The probabilities that they pass the exams are shown in the table.

What is the probability that

a all 3 girls pass the theory exam

b all 3 girls fail the practical exam

c Holly passes all 3 exams

d 2 of the girls pass the teaching exam but the other one fails

e Polly passes only one of the 3 exams?

	Theory	Practical	Teaching
Polly	0.6	0.9	0.7
Holly	0.4	0.6	0.8
Lily	0.5	0.8	0.6

A* **1** A box contains 6 caramel-centred chocolates and 8 nut-centred chocolates.

Ruth takes two chocolates from the box at random.

a Draw a tree diagram to show all the possible outcomes.

b What is the probability that the two chocolates that Ruth takes have
  i the same centre
  ii different centres?

A* **2** There are 16 girls and 14 boys in Class 11B.

A02 Three students are selected at random.

What is the probability that two of the students are girls and one is a boy?

A* **3** Class 10C has two quiz teams.

There are 6 students in each team.

Team A has 2 girls and 4 boys. Team B has 3 girls and 3 boys.

Step 1: A student is chosen at random from Team A and moved to Team B.

Step 2: A student is chosen at random from Team B and moved to Team A.

A03 Work out the probability that Team A has more boys than girls after these two steps.

Key Points

Drawing and using a cumulative frequency diagram for grouped data　B

Cumulative frequency is a running total of the frequencies.

You can use a cumulative frequency diagram to estimate the median, the lower quartile and the upper quartile.

median $= \frac{n}{2}$th value　　lower quartile $= \frac{n}{4}$th value

upper quartile $= \frac{3n}{4}$th value

The inter-quartile range indicates the spread of the data.

inter-quartile range = upper quartile − lower quartile

Drawing a box plot from a cumulative frequency diagram　B

A box plot shows the range, the lower and upper quartiles, and the median of a set of data.

Box plots must be drawn on the same scale as the cumulative frequency diagram from which the data comes.

Comparing data sets and drawing conclusions　B

The median is one of the measures of 'average'. Always look to compare the medians.

The inter-quartile range is a measure of consistency and tells you the spread of the middle 50% of the data. Always comment on the sizes of the inter-quartile ranges of the distributions.

6.1　Cumulative frequency

1 Elton organised a sponsored 'walk for life' event.

Entrants walked as far as they wanted to, up to a maximum of 12 km.

The table shows the distances walked during the event.

Distance, d (km)	$0 < d \leqslant 2$	$2 < d \leqslant 4$	$4 < d \leqslant 6$	$6 < d \leqslant 8$	$8 < d \leqslant 10$	$10 < d \leqslant 12$
Frequency	75	102	61	32	27	3

a　Draw a cumulative frequency diagram to illustrate this data.

b　Use your cumulative frequency diagram to estimate
　　i　the median distance
　　ii　the lower quartile
　　iii　the upper quartile
　　iv　the inter-quartile range

Entrants who walked up to 3 km collected, on average, £15 each.

c　Estimate the total amount raised by the entrants who walked up to 3 km.

Entrants who walked over $6\frac{1}{2}$ km collected, on average, £23 each.

d　Estimate the total amount raised by the entrants who walked over $6\frac{1}{2}$ km.

B

1 For each of these box plots, work out

    i the median

    ii the upper quartile

    iii the inter-quartile range

    iv the largest data value

    v the range.

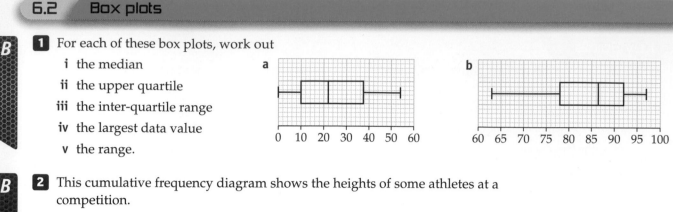

B

2 This cumulative frequency diagram shows the heights of some athletes at a competition.

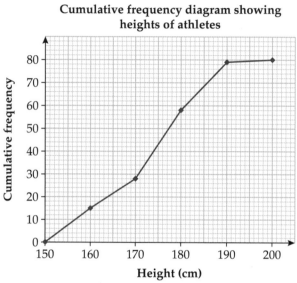

a How many athletes were measured?

b Estimate the median height of these athletes.

c Estimate the inter-quartile range of this data. Show your working.

d Draw a box plot to represent this data.

A02   **e** Estimate the range of the heights of the tallest 25% of the athletes.

6.3   Comparing data sets and drawing conclusions

B

1 The box plots show the weight of coffee in 200 jars produced by Machine 1, and in 120 jars produced by Machine 2.

    a What is the median weight produced by Machine 1?

    b What is the maximum weight produced by Machine 2?

    c Write **three** comments comparing the weight of coffee produced by Machine 1 and Machine 2.

A02

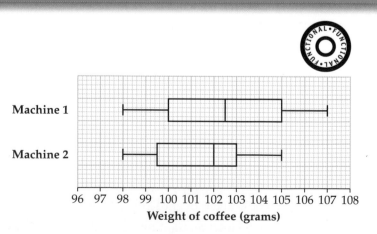

2 The lifetimes of two types of low-energy light bulb were measured. The cumulative frequency distributions of both types are shown on the diagram.

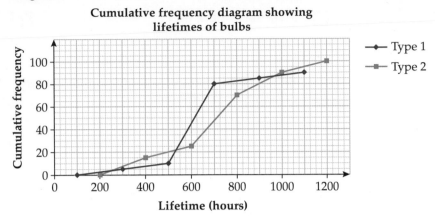

a How many Type 1 bulbs were tested?

b Estimate the minimum and maximum lifetimes of Type 1 bulbs.

c Estimate the median for the Type 1 bulbs.

d Estimate the inter-quartile range for the Type 1 bulbs.

e How many of the Type 2 bulbs were tested?

f Estimate the minimum and maximum lifetimes of Type 2 bulbs.

g Estimate the median for the Type 2 bulbs.

h Estimate the inter-quartile range for the Type 2 bulbs.

i Draw box plots for both types of bulb. Use a scale of 0 to 1200 on the horizontal axis. Draw one box plot directly beneath the other.

j Compare the two types of bulbs, giving reasons for any statements you make.

AO3

Links to:

Higher Student Book
Ch7, pp.105–125

Key Points

Writing a ratio as a fraction   **D**

The numerator is the part of the ratio you've been asked about. The denominator is the total number of parts of the ratio.

Divide a quantity in a given ratio   **D** **C**

To share in a given ratio

1 Work out the total number of parts to be shared into.

2 Work out the value of one part.

3 Work out the value of each share.

Writing ratios in the form $1:n$ or $n:1$ **C**

First decide which number in the ratio you want to be 1, then divide all the numbers in the ratio by that number.

Direct proportion   **D**

When two values are in direct proportion

- if one value is zero, so is the other
- if one value doubles, so does the other.

Unitary method   **D**

To solve proportion problems using the unitary method, work out the value of one unit first.

Best buys   **D** **C**

The 'best buy' is the product that gives you the best value for money.

To compare two prices and sizes, work out the price for one unit for each size.

Inverse proportion   **C** **B**

When two values are in inverse proportion, one increases at the same rate as the other decreases.

Writing and using equations to solve direct proportion problems   **A**

$\propto$ means 'is proportional to'.

You can write an equation using k as the constant of proportionality.

y varies as x	$y \propto x$	equation $y = kx$
y varies as x^2	$y \propto x^2$	equation $y = kx^2$
y varies as $\sqrt{x}$	$y \propto \sqrt{x}$	equation $y = k\sqrt{x}$

Writing and using equations to solve inverse proportion problems   **A**

You can write an equation using k as the constant of proportionality.

y varies as the inverse of x

$$y \propto \frac{1}{x} \qquad \text{equation } y = \frac{k}{x}$$

y varies as the inverse of x^2

$$y \propto \frac{1}{x^2} \qquad \text{equation } y = \frac{k}{x^2}$$

y varies as the inverse of $\sqrt{x}$

$$y \propto \frac{1}{\sqrt{x}} \qquad \text{equation } y = \frac{k}{\sqrt{x}}$$

7.1   Using ratios

D

1 These are some of the ingredients that Jan uses to make 8 mini-cakes.

Work out the quantities that Jan uses to make

  a   24 mini-cakes

  b   4 mini-cakes

  c   12 mini-cakes.

600 g flour
150 g sugar
50 g raisins

2 In a typing test, Tim managed an average speed of 42 words per minute.

  a   How long does it take Tim to type 112 words?

  b   How many words would you expect Tim to type in 100 seconds?

D

3 Here is a recipe for fishcakes.

Steve has 2.1 kg of fish fillets. He uses them all to make fishcakes.

  a   How much of each of the other ingredients does Steve use?

AO2   **b**   How many people will Steve's fishcakes serve?

Fishcakes (serves 4)
600 g fish fillets
2 tbsp sunflower oil
500 g potatoes
2 medium eggs

7.2 Ratios and fractions

1 Alfi and Michael share a pasty in the ratio 2 : 3.

   a What fraction of the pasty does Alfi have?

   b What fraction of the pasty does Michael have?

2 The ratio of lorries to other vehicles on a cross-channel ferry is 3 : 4.

   Jim says, 'Three-quarters of the vehicles are lorries.'

   Is he correct? Explain your answer.

3 A recipe for apple and rhubarb crumble uses apple and rhubarb in the ratio 5 : 2.

   Ros uses 475 g of apple in her apple and rhubarb crumble.

   What mass of rhubarb does she use?

4 A mobile phone shop sells contract phones and pay-as-you-go phones in the ratio 8 : 3.

   Last month 184 contract phones were sold. How many phones were sold altogether?

7.3 Ratios in the form 1 : n or n : 1

1 Write each of the following ratios in the form

   i 1 : n **ii** n : 1

   a 6 : 15   **b** 12 : 8   **c** 10 : 16

   d 20 : 9   **e** £1.80 : £2.40   **f** 5 m : 2 cm

   g 5 years : 4 months   **h** 4 g : 5 kg   **i** 2 l : 400 ml

2 The ratio of additives to water in one make of orange squash is 17 : 210.

   a Write this as a ratio in the form n : 1.

   The ratio of additives to water in a second make of orange squash is 3 : 37.

   b Write this as a ratio in the form n : 1.

   c Compare your answers to parts **a** and **b**. Which make of squash, the first or the second, has the higher proportion of water? Explain your answer.

3 The ratio of fruit : flour : butter in one type of fruit scone is 33 : 59 : 9.

   The ratio of fruit : flour : butter in another type of fruit scone is 11 : 23 : 4.

   Which fruit scone has the higher proportion of fruit? Show working to support your answer.

7.4 Working with ratios

1 Share £70 in each of the following ratios.

   a 1 : 6   **b** 1 : 9   **c** 13 : 1

2 Share £70 in each of the following ratios.

   a 3 : 7   **b** 10 : 4   **c** 3 : 10 : 22

3 Adam and Craig buy a bag of pencils from a shop.

   Adam pays 70p and Craig pays 80p.

   a Write down the amounts they pay as a ratio in its lowest terms.

   There are 30 pencils in the bag. They share the pencils in the same ratio as the amounts they paid.

   b Work out how many pencils they each have.

4 In a recipe for raspberry compote, every 2 kg of raspberries is mixed with 1.75 kg sugar.

Reth has 5 kg of raspberries. How much sugar does he need?

5 Tanya and Shona buy an antique chair for £750.

Tanya pays £300 and Shona pays the rest.

They sell the chair at auction for £420, and share the money in the same ratio as the amounts they paid to buy it.

How much money has each of them lost?

7.5 Proportion

1 Gill works 7 hours a day. During this time she does a quality check on 84 cars.

She is asked to do 2 hours overtime. How many cars should she be able to quality check during this overtime?

2 Mr Ellis buys 30 textbooks for his class. The total cost is £442.50.

Mr Ellis only has 26 students in his class. How much money could Mr Ellis have saved if he had only bought 26 textbooks?

3 Mr Reed works for 35 hours per week and earns £770.

Mrs Khan works for 152 hours per month and earns £3268.

Who has the greater wage per hour? Show your working.

4 Here are 3 bottles of banana smoothie.

Which bottle of smoothie is the best value for money?

Show your working.

7.6 Inverse proportion

1 It takes 2 people 15 hours to proofread a complete maths book.

How long would it take 3 people?

2 It takes 5 horses 36 minutes to eat 1 bale of hay.

How long would it take 3 horses to eat a similar size bale of hay?

3 A cake manufacturer has an order for 5000 cakes.

All the cakes must be cooked in 7 hours.

One oven can cook 125 cakes in 1 hour.

How many ovens need to be used in order to cook all the cakes?

4 Vicky is laying new tiles on her kitchen floor.

There were 180 old tiles on the floor. Each tile covered 625 cm².

Each new tile covers an area of 900 cm².

How many of the new tiles does she need?

7.7 Writing equations for direct proportion problems

1 x is directly proportional to y.

When $x = 20$, $y = 4$.

Work out

  a x when $y = 3$ **b** y when $x = 10$.

2 c varies as d.

When $c = 3$, $d = 45$.

Work out

  a c when $d = 37.5$ **b** d when $c = 10$.

3 The distance, d, travelled by a ship is directly proportional to the time taken, t.

The ship travels 42 nautical miles in 4 hours.

  a Write an equation connecting d and t.

  b Work out d, when $t = 24$.

  c Work out t, when $d = 10$. Give your answer to the nearest minute.

4 In an experiment, P is found to be proportional to t^2.
Work out the missing values from the table.

P		27	151.25
t	2	3	

5 The mass of a ball bearing is proportional to the cube of its radius.

A ball bearing of radius 3 mm has a mass of 48.9 g.

  a What will be the mass of a ball bearing of radius 4 mm? Give your answer to the nearest gram.

  b What is the radius of a ball bearing with a mass of 391.2 g?

7.8 Writing equations for inverse proportion problems

1 e is inversely proportional to f.

When $e = 6$, $f = 2$.

Work out

  a e, when $f = 6$ **b** f, when $e = 27$.

2 g is inversely proportional to $\sqrt{h}$.

When $h = 9$, $g = 1$.

Work out

  a g, when $h = 100$ **b** h, when $g = 6$.

3 i varies inversely as the cube of j.
Copy and complete this table.

i		200	12.8
j	0.8	2	

4 The time taken to cook food in a microwave oven is inversely proportional to the power of the microwave.

A 500 watt oven takes 12 minutes to cook a pie.

  a Write an equation relating the time taken, t, to the power, P.

  b How long will it take a 400 watt microwave to cook a similar pie?

  c How long will it take a 600 watt microwave to cook a similar pie?

  d What power microwave will be needed to cook a similar pie in 8 minutes?

Key Points

Repeated percentage change [C]

Generally, when you invest money, the interest is calculated on the amount invested in the first place plus any interest already received. This is known as compound interest.

1 Add the rate of interest to 100%.
2 Convert this percentage to a decimal to get the multiplier.
3 Multiply the original amount by the multiplier as many times as the number of years for which the money is invested.

You can also use this method to work out a repeated percentage loss or depreciation, except that to find the multiplier you must first subtract the percentage from 100%.

Reverse percentages [B]

To work out the original quantity when you are given the quantity after a percentage increase or decrease, use one of these methods.

Method A

1 Work out what percentage the final quantity represents.
2 Divide by this percentage to find 1%.
3 Multiply by 100 to get the 100% figure.

Method B

1 Work out what percentage the final quantity represents.
2 Divide by 100 to get the multiplier.
3 Divide the final quantity by the multiplier.

Using and interpreting standard form [B]

A number in standard form is a number between 1 and 10 ($1 \leqslant n < 10$) multiplied by an integer power of 10.

Finding the upper and lower bounds [C] [B] [A]

The upper and lower bounds are given to one more degree of accuracy than the rounded value.

The upper bound of 220 people to the nearest 10 is 224 people (as this is discrete data).

The upper bound of 220 cm to the nearest 10 cm is 225 cm (as this is continuous data).

Calculating absolute and percentage error [A] [A*]

The nominal value is the value that a quantity is supposed to be if there were no errors.

The absolute error is the difference between the measured value and the nominal value.

The percentage error is found by finding the absolute error as a percentage of the nominal value.

$$\text{percentage error} = \frac{\text{absolute error}}{\text{nominal value}} \times 100\%$$

8.1   Repeated percentage change

C

1 Jock invests £2500 for 3 years at a rate of 6% per annum compound interest.
How much will his investment be worth at the end of the 3 years?
Give your answer to the nearest pound.

2 Havel buys a new car for £8995. Each year the value of the car depreciates by 12%.
What will the car be worth at the end of 3 years, to the nearest pound?

C

3 When Maria was born, her uncle put £1000 into an investment account for her.
For the first 10 years, the money earned a compound interest of 12% per annum.
After that it earned a compound interest of 7% per annum.
How much was the investment worth on her 18th birthday, to the nearest pound?

4 How many years will it take £100 to grow to £200 at a compound interest rate of 5% per year?

5 Sam invested £2250 at a fixed rate of compound interest.
After 4 years his investment was worth £3176.
What was the rate of compound interest Sam received?

A02

8.2 Reverse percentages

B

1 After a pay rise of 2.5%, Josh earns £12 812.50.

What did he earn before his pay rise?

2 A netbook is reduced by 22% in a sale.

Its price is now £253.50. What was its price before the sale?

3 A bamboo plant increased its height by 48% in 24 hours.

At the end of the 24 hours it was 518 mm high. How high was it at the start of the 24 hours?

B

4 At one school, 14% of the students had the flu on the same day.

The remaining 731 students did not have the flu. What is the total number of students at this school?

5 When a metal rod is dipped into liquid nitrogen, it shrinks by $2\frac{1}{5}$%.

A metal rod is 48.9 cm long immediately after it has been dipped.

a What was the original length of the rod before it was dipped?

Five minutes after removing the metal rod from the liquid nitrogen, it is still $1\frac{1}{2}$% shorter than its original length.

b How long is the metal rod at this time?

A02

8.3 Standard form

B

1 Write the following numbers in standard form.

  a 50 000   **b** 500   **c** 51   **d** 51 000 000

  e 0.5   **f** 0.000 05   **g** 0.005 13   **h** 0.0503

2 Write the following as decimal numbers.

  a 2×10^3 **b** 2×10^{-6} **c** 2.46×10^8 **d** 2.46×10^{-1}

3 Rewrite these numbers in standard form.

  a 23.6×10^2 **b** 0.02×10^3 **c** 23.6×10^{-4} **d** 0.002×10^{-4}

  e 2.7 million   **f** $\frac{5}{8}$ **g** $23 \times 10^3 \times 0.032$ **h** $\sqrt{1600 \times 25}$

4 Use a calculator to work out the following. Give your answers in standard form.

  a $(4.8 \times 10^3) \times (7.2 \times 10^8)$ **b** $\dfrac{2.6 \times 10^3}{1.3 \times 10^{-4}}$

5 The radius of the Moon is approximately 1.73×10^3 km.

The formula for the volume of a sphere is $\frac{4}{3}\pi r^3$.

Find the volume of the Moon. Give your answer in standard form to a suitable degree of accuracy.

6 Light travels at 3×10^8 metres per second.

Work out the length, in km, of a light year.

B

A02

8.4 Upper and lower bounds

C

1 Write down the range of possible values of the following.

  a 280 children to the nearest 10 children.   **b** 280 m to the nearest 1 m.

  c £100 to the nearest £10.   **d** 2.8 m to the nearest tenth of a metre.

2 Mark loads 20 identical boxes into a van.

Each box weighs 8.6 kg correct to one decimal place.

What is the smallest possible total weight of the boxes?

3 A box contains 10 identical square floor tiles.

Each tile has a side length of 24 cm measured to the nearest cm.

What is the difference between the maximum and minimum floor areas that these 10 tiles could cover?

4 Sound travels at 330 m/s (metres per second), to the nearest 10 m/s.

Angus sees a flash of lightning and hears the thunder 7.3 seconds later, measured to the nearest $\frac{1}{10}$ of a second.

What is the closest distance that the lightning could be from Angus?

5 This is part of Eric's homework.

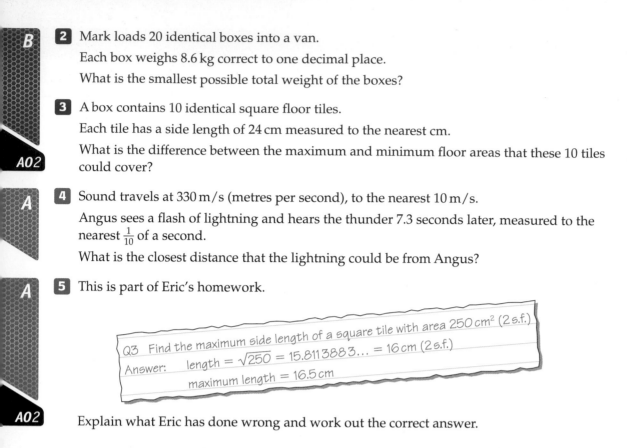

Q3 Find the maximum side length of a square tile with area 250 cm² (2 s.f.)

Answer: length = √250 = 15.8113883... = 16 cm (2 s.f.)

maximum length = 16.5 cm

Explain what Eric has done wrong and work out the correct answer.

8.5   Error

1 Jonathan was supposed to cut a 2.3 m length of wood for a shelf.

When he measured the piece, it was actually 2.28 m long. Work out the percentage error.

2 Arlene was asked to estimate 10 seconds.

Her estimate was timed at 11.2 seconds. Work out the percentage error.

3 A rectangular tile has sides of 15.0 cm and 7.5 cm.

Both measurements are correct to one decimal place.

Work out

a   the nominal area of the tile

b   the upper and lower bounds of the lengths of the sides

c   the least and greatest possible areas of the tile

d   the maximum absolute error

e   the maximum percentage error.

4 A drinks dispenser advertises a 220 ml cup of hot chocolate, with a possible error of 2%.

Jim says, 'The machine will dispense between 215.6 ml and 224.4 ml.'

Is he correct? Show working to support your answer.

5 Jeff has three pieces of wood to glue together to make a worktop.

One piece is 1.2 m long, the second is 2.4 m long and the third is 40 cm long.

All measurements are correct to the nearest 10 cm.

What is the maximum percentage error in the total length of the worktop?

Key Points

Estimating **D** **C**

You can use estimation to check that an answer is about right.

To estimate

1 Round all the numbers to one significant figure.

2 Do the calculation using these approximations.

Currency conversion **D** **C**

To change an amount in pounds sterling to another currency you need to multiply by the exchange rate.

To change an amount in another currency to pounds sterling you need to divide by the exchange rate.

9.1 Estimation

1 Estimate the answer to each of the following. Show your working. **D**

a $\dfrac{279 + 109}{196}$ b $\dfrac{279 \times 109}{196}$ c $\dfrac{2.79 + 1.09}{3.52 - 1.46}$

2 Estimate the answer to each of the following. Show your working. **C**

a $\dfrac{12.3 \times 27.3}{0.19}$ b $\dfrac{747 \times 2.62}{0.3 \times 10.3}$ c $\dfrac{31.8 \times 81.01}{(2.125 + 6.93) \times 18.95}$

3 Look at this calculation. **C**

$$\dfrac{3.7 \times 812.11}{27.33 + 61.81 - 12.5}$$

Ruth and Gordon use calculators to work it out.

Ruth gets an answer of 39.2 and Gordon gets 29.6.

Use approximation to decide who is more likely to be correct.

4 Use approximation to estimate the value of

$$\dfrac{78.44 \times 20.5}{3.75^2}$$

5 Which is the better approximation? **C**

A $\dfrac{5.3^2}{3.79 \times 23.39} \approx \dfrac{5^2}{4 \times 20}$ **B** $\dfrac{5.3^2}{3.79 \times 23.39} \approx \dfrac{5^2}{4 \times 23}$

Give a reason for your answer.

6 A 1 kg pot of tile adhesive is just enough to lay 27 floor tiles.

Richard needs to lay 245 tiles in one room.

a Which is the best approximate calculation to use to work out the number of pots of tile adhesive that Richard needs to buy? Give a reason for your answer.

     A $200 \div 30$ **B** $200 \div 20$ **C** $240 \div 30$ **D** $250 \div 25$

b Richard needs to lay tiles in another room. This room is half the size of the one in part **a**.

Use estimation to decide how many pots of tile adhesive Richard needs to buy for this room.

AO2

7 Xavier is travelling on a motorway in his car. He sees a sign that tells him that the distance to the next service station is 75 km. His car has 4.45 litres of fuel in the tank. He knows that his car can travel 17.3 km per litre of fuel. **C**

Use estimation to decide whether Xavier has enough fuel to get to the service station.

AO3

D

1 The exchange rate between the pound (£) and the US dollar (US$) is £1 = $1.60.

  a How many US$ would you get for £280?

  b How many pounds would you get for $280?

2 The exchange rate between the pound (£) and the South Korean Won is £1 = 1850 Won.

  a How many South Korean Won would you get for £350?

  b How many pounds would you get for 1 million Won?

C

3 A Japanese tourist in London wants to buy a suit in Savile Row.

The price of the suit is £1250. The exchange rate is £1 = 145 yen.

  a What is the price of the suit in yen?

A week later the price of the same suit is 171 250 yen.

  b What is the new exchange rate?

C

4 In London, a bottle of perfume is priced at £55. In Los Angeles the same bottle costs US$90. In Mumbai, the same bottle costs 3900 Rupees.

The exchange rates are £1 = US$1.60 and £1 = 75 Rupees.

Where is the perfume the cheapest?

5 Every year Jamie goes to Spain for a holiday.

He always changes £300 to euros (€).

Last year the exchange rate was £1 = €1.24.

This year the exchange rate is £1 = €1.16.

How many fewer euros did Jamie have this year compared with last year?

6 Bardo is going to visit his family in Denmark.

He changes £750 into Danish Kroner (DKK).

  a How many DKK does Bardo get?

During his visit he spends 5539 DKK.

When he gets back to the UK he changes his remaining DKK into pounds.

  b How many pounds does Bardo receive?

Exchange rates		
We sell:	£1 →	8.2 DKK
We buy:	9.4 DKK →	£1

AO2

Links to:
Higher Student Book
Ch10, pp.156–164

Key Points

Finding multiples and LCMs **D** **C**

Multiples of a number divide exactly by that number.

The lowest common multiple (LCM) of two numbers is the smallest number that is a multiple of both numbers.

Factors and HCFs **D** **C**

The factors of a number are the numbers that divide into it exactly.

The highest common factor (HCF) of two numbers is the largest number that is a factor of both numbers.

Squares, cubes and roots **D** **C**

To square a number you multiply it by itself.

The inverse of squaring is finding the square root ($\sqrt{}$)
Positive numbers have two square roots: a positive square root and a negative square root.

The inverse of cubing is finding the cube root ($\sqrt[3]{}$)

Writing a number as a product of prime factors **C**

You can write any number as a product of **prime factors**.

You can use a factor tree to write a number as a product of prime factors.

$60 = 2 \times 2 \times 3 \times 5$

You can write this using index notation as $60 = 2^2 \times 3 \times 5$.

You can also use repeated division to write a number as a product of prime factors.

$60 = 2^2 \times 3 \times 5$

$$
\begin{array}{c|c}
2 & 60 \\
2 & 30 \\
3 & 15 \\
5 & 5 \\
\hline
& 1
\end{array}
$$

Using prime factors to find HCFs and LCMs **C**

To find the HCF

1 Write each number as the product of its prime factors.

2 Find the prime factors that are common to both lists of prime factors numbers.

3 Multiply these to give the HCF.

To find the LCM

1 Write each number as the product of its prime factors.

2 For each prime factor, find the higher power in the two lists of prime factors.

3 Multiply these to give the LCM.

10.1 Lowest common multiples

1 **a** Write down the first 10 multiples of 8.
   b Write the first 10 multiples of 12.
   c Write three common multiples of 8 and 12.
   d Write the LCM of 8 and 12.

   D

2 Andrew has some 20p coins. Zak has some 50p coins.
   They both have the same amount of money.
   What is the smallest amount of money that they both could have?

   C

3 Bailey and Yasmin are the same age.
   Bailey says, 'Our ages are a multiple of 6.'
   Yasmin says, 'Our ages are a multiple of 9.'
   What is the youngest age that they both could be?

   A02

10.2 Highest common factors

1 **a** Write the factors of 8.
   b Write the factors of 12.
   c Write all the common factors of 8 and 12.
   d Write the HCF of 8 and 24.

   D

2 A 2p piece and a 10p piece are the same height.

Carole has 64 2p pieces and 48 10p pieces.

She arranges her coins into stacks. Each stack contains only 2p pieces or only 10p pieces. All the stacks are the same height.

What is the largest possible number of coins in each stack?

3 Jill has two lengths of gold chain.

One is 672 cm long and one is 720 cm long.

She wants to cut them into pieces the same length to make necklaces, which are as long as possible.

She wants to use all the chain. What length should she cut them into?

10.3   Squares, cubes and roots

1 Write down the answers to the following.

   a 5^2 **b** $(-5)^2$ **c** $\sqrt{64}$

   d $\sqrt[3]{27}$ **e** $-\sqrt{100}$ **f** $\sqrt[3]{1}$

2 Write these numbers in order of size, smallest first.

   $\sqrt{4^3}$ 2^2 $\sqrt{144}$ $\sqrt[3]{2^3}$ $\sqrt{10^2}$

3 Davina is making patterns with mosaic tiles.

She has used all of her tiles to make three square patterns.

One of her square patterns has 13 tiles along one side, another has 6 tiles along one side and the other has 5 tiles along one side.

She decides to make the biggest square she can with all of her tiles.

Show, that after making the biggest square she can, she will have enough tiles left over to make the first two square number patterns.

4 Work out $\sqrt{13^2 - 12^2}$

5 Write $\dfrac{4^3}{6^3}$ as a fraction in its lowest terms.

6 Ed is making cubes with 1 cm³ blocks.

He has made the first five cube numbers using all of his blocks.

He decides to make the biggest cube he can with all his blocks.

He uses the rest to make a square pattern.

What is the side length of his square pattern?

10.4   Prime factors

1 Write 30 as a product of prime factors.

2 Write 360 as a product of prime factors. Give your answer in index form.

3 Use prime factors to work out the highest common factor (HCF) of 60 and 96.

4 Use prime factors to work out the lowest common multiple (LCM) of 30 and 48.

5 Emyr buys blank CDs in packs of 50. He buys CD cases in packs of 12.

What is the smallest number of each that he must buy so that every CD has a case, and there are no CDs or cases left over?

6 Frank has a collection of 2p pieces.

He arranges his collection into piles of 18. There are none left over.

He then arranges his collection into piles of 20. There are none left over.

What is the smallest amount of money that Frank could have?

Links to:
Higher Student Book
Ch11, pp.165–176

Key Points

Comparing fractions **D**

To compare fractions, change them to equivalent fractions with the same denominator.

Adding and subtracting fractions **D**

You can add or subtract fractions only when they have the same denominator.

You can use equivalent fractions to do this. For example,
$\frac{1}{2} + \frac{1}{3} = \frac{3}{6} + \frac{2}{6} = \frac{5}{6}$

Adding and subtracting mixed numbers **C**

You can add or subtract mixed numbers by changing them into improper fractions.

For example, $1\frac{1}{2} + 3\frac{2}{5} = \frac{4}{9} + \frac{17}{5} = \frac{20}{19} + \frac{51}{15} = \frac{71}{15} = 4\frac{11}{15}$

Finding reciprocals **C**

When two numbers can be multiplied together to give the answer 1, then each number is called the reciprocal of the other.

The reciprocal of a fraction is found by turning the fraction upside down.

The reciprocal of a number is 1 divided by that number.

Multiplying fractions and mixed numbers **D** **C** **B**

To multiply mixed numbers, change them to improper fractions first.

For example, $4\frac{1}{3} \times \frac{2}{5} = \frac{13}{3} \times \frac{2}{5} = \frac{13 \times 2}{3 \times 5} = \frac{26}{15} = 1\frac{11}{15}$

Dividing by fractions and mixed numbers **D** **C** **B**

To divide by a fraction, turn the fraction upside down and multiply.

When the division involves mixed numbers, change them to improper fractions first.

For example, $\frac{3}{4} \div 7 = \frac{3}{4} \div \frac{7}{1} = \frac{3}{4} \times \frac{1}{7} = \frac{3 \times 1}{4 \times 7} = \frac{3}{28}$.

11.1   Comparing fractions

1 Which of these fractions is closest to $\frac{3}{4}$?

   A $\frac{7}{10}$ **B** $\frac{23}{30}$ **C** $\frac{4}{5}$ **D** $\frac{33}{40}$ **D**

2 Put each of these sets of fractions in order of size, smallest first. **D**

   a $\frac{5}{6}$, $\frac{2}{3}$, $\frac{7}{9}$ **b** $\frac{1}{3}$, $\frac{3}{10}$, $\frac{4}{15}$

3 Shen has these three fraction cards.

Shen says, 'If I put them in order of size, starting with the smallest, I get $\frac{7}{12}$, $\frac{8}{15}$, $\frac{17}{30}$.'

Tao says, 'You're wrong, the order should be $\frac{8}{15}$, $\frac{7}{12}$, $\frac{17}{30}$.'

Is either of them correct? Give a reason for your answer. **A02**

4 Ted says, 'I am thinking of a fraction. My fraction is bigger than $\frac{3}{5}$, but smaller than $\frac{7}{10}$. Both the numerator and denominator of my fraction are two-digit square numbers. What is the fraction I am thinking of?' **D**

5 Penny says, 'I am thinking of a fraction. My fraction is bigger than $\frac{2}{3}$, but smaller than $\frac{3}{4}$. The numerator of my fraction is a prime number. The denominator of my fraction is 1 less than a square number. What is the fraction I am thinking of?' **A03**

D

1 Work out

    a $\frac{3}{5} - \frac{1}{4}$ **b** $\frac{1}{2} + \frac{4}{9}$ **c** $\frac{9}{10} - \frac{7}{12}$ **d** $\frac{2}{11} + \frac{3}{7}$

D

2 Bill wants to make a shelf that is $\frac{9}{10}$ m long.

    He has two pieces of wood. One is $\frac{1}{5}$ m long and the other is $\frac{5}{8}$ m long.

    Bill says, 'If I join the two pieces of wood together the total length will be long enough to make the shelf.'

    Is he correct? Show working to support your decision.

3 Alicia is making two cakes. She needs $\frac{1}{3}$ kg of sultanas for each cake.

    She has two bags of sultanas. One bag contains $\frac{1}{4}$ kg and the other contains $\frac{3}{8}$ kg.

    Does Alicia have enough sultanas to make both cakes?

A02

    Show working to support your decision.

D

4 Mai has two fraction cards.

    Both the fractions are positive. $\boxed{\frac{?}{6}}$ $\boxed{\frac{?}{8}}$

    Mai adds the two fractions and gets an answer that simplifies to $\frac{13}{24}$.

    Could Mai's answer be correct?

    Show working to support your decision.

5 Stefan has three fractions cards.

    $\boxed{\frac{?}{24}}$ $\boxed{\frac{?}{16}}$ $\boxed{\frac{?}{6}}$

    All the fractions are positive.

    He adds the three fractions and gets an answer that cancels to $\frac{1}{4}$.

A03

    Could his answer be correct? Show working to support your decision.

11.3   Adding and subtracting with mixed numbers

C

1 Work out

    a $7\frac{1}{2} + 4\frac{1}{8}$ **b** $3\frac{3}{5} + 2\frac{7}{15}$ **c** $1\frac{2}{3} + 3\frac{4}{7}$

    d $4\frac{1}{4} - 1\frac{7}{10}$ **e** $5\frac{4}{5} - 2\frac{2}{3} + 3\frac{1}{2}$ **f** $2\frac{5}{6} + 2\frac{3}{4} - 1\frac{5}{8}$

C

2 Harvey swims a total of $5\frac{1}{2}$ miles in the swimming pool every week.

    He swims $2\frac{1}{3}$ miles of front crawl and $1\frac{4}{5}$ miles of breaststroke. The rest of the distance he swims backstroke.

A02

    How many miles of backstroke does he swim each week?

C

3 Ella adds together two mixed numbers. The fractions have different denominators.

    Ella gets an answer of $2\frac{11}{18}$.

    Suggest two different pairs of mixed numbers that Ella may have added.

C

4 Martin adds together two mixed numbers. The fractions have different denominators.

    Martin gets an answer of $3\frac{1}{24}$.

A03

    Suggest two different pairs of mixed numbers that Martin may have added.

5 Claude has two mixed-number cards.

$$6\frac{?}{4} \quad 2\frac{?}{9}$$

Both the mixed numbers are positive.

He adds the mixed numbers and gets an answer that cancels to $8\frac{1}{3}$.

Could his answer be correct? Show working to support your decision.

6 Sandra wants to buy a horse trailer that can carry two horses. She sees one advertised in the local paper.

The maximum weight her car can tow is $2\frac{3}{5}$ tonnes.

The trailer weighs $\frac{9}{10}$ tonne. Her horses weigh $\frac{1}{2}$ tonne and $\frac{4}{5}$ tonne.

Is this trailer suitable for Sandra? Show working to support your decision.

11.4   Multiplying mixed numbers

1 Work out these multiplications.
Give your answers as mixed numbers when possible.

a $3 \times 2\frac{2}{5}$ b $5 \times 2\frac{5}{8}$ c $4\frac{4}{7} \times 7$ d $1\frac{5}{9} \times 3$

2 One radiator has a mass of $9\frac{2}{5}$ kg. Three of these radiators are packed into one crate.
A packing crate has a mass of $4\frac{1}{2}$ kg. Two full crates are packed into a van.
What is the total weight of the radiators and crates that are packed into the van?

3 Work out these multiplications.
Simplify your answers and write them as mixed numbers when possible.

a $\frac{1}{2} \times 3\frac{4}{5}$ b $\frac{2}{3} \times 2\frac{3}{5}$ c $5\frac{1}{4} \times \frac{4}{7}$ d $1\frac{5}{6} \times \frac{3}{8}$

4 Brendan is going to fit some laminate flooring.

Each strip of flooring is $\frac{2}{5}$ m wide.

The length of the flooring he needs is $32\frac{3}{4}$ m.

a What is the area of the laminate flooring that Brendan needs?

The price of the laminate flooring is £42.50 per square metre.

It can only be bought in a whole number of square metres.

b How much does Brendan pay for the laminate flooring?

area of rectangle = length × width

5 Kelly works from home. She makes leather belts and dog collars.
It takes her, on average, $1\frac{1}{4}$ hours to make 1 belt, and $1\frac{2}{3}$ hours to make 1 dog collar.
She has an order for 3 belts and 2 dog collars. She must complete the order in 1 day.
She stops for $\frac{1}{2}$ hour for lunch and for $\frac{1}{4}$ hour for a coffee break. She starts work at 9 am.
Will she complete the order by 5 pm?

6 Work out these multiplications. Simplify your answers, and write them as mixed numbers when possible.

a $3\frac{1}{3} \times 1\frac{3}{5}$ b $2\frac{3}{4} \times 2\frac{2}{7}$ c $4\frac{5}{6} \times 2\frac{2}{5}$ d $1\frac{3}{7} \times 4\frac{1}{5}$

7 A vegetable plot measures $6\frac{3}{4}$ m by $9\frac{1}{3}$ m. What is its area?

C

1 **a** Find the reciprocal of each of these numbers.

Give your answers as fractions, whole numbers or mixed numbers.

i 5   **ii** 15   **iii** 40   **iv** $\frac{1}{4}$ **v** $\frac{3}{8}$ **vi** $\frac{7}{9}$

b Check your answers to part **a** by multiplying each number by its reciprocal.
The answer to each multiplication should be 1.

2 Find the reciprocal of each of these numbers.

Give your answers as fractions, whole numbers or mixed numbers. Show all your working.

a 0.2   **b** 0.7   **c** 0.08   **d** 3.4

C

3 This is part of Emyr's homework.

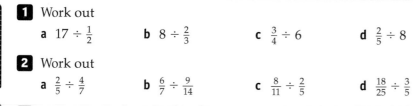

Find the reciprocal of 0.48.

$$\frac{1}{0.48} = \frac{1 \times 100}{0.48 \times 100} = \frac{100}{48} = \frac{100 \div 4}{48 \div 4} = \frac{25}{4}$$

$$\text{Reciprocal} = \frac{4}{25}$$

AO2

Has Emyr got this question right or wrong? Explain your answer.

11.6   Dividing fractions

D

1 Work out

a $17 \div \frac{1}{2}$ **b** $8 \div \frac{2}{3}$ **c** $\frac{3}{4} \div 6$ **d** $\frac{2}{5} \div 8$

2 Work out

a $\frac{2}{5} \div \frac{4}{7}$ **b** $\frac{6}{7} \div \frac{9}{14}$ **c** $\frac{8}{11} \div \frac{2}{5}$ **d** $\frac{18}{25} \div \frac{3}{5}$

C

3 Colin shares $1\frac{1}{2}$ fruit cakes between 15 people. How much do they each receive?

4 Karine's dog eats $\frac{3}{8}$ kg of dog food each day. One sack of dog food weighs $2\frac{1}{2}$ kg.

a For how many days can Karine feed her dog with one sack of dog food?

b At the end of the number of days found in part **a**, how much dog food will Karine have left over?

AO2

c What is the smallest number of sacks that Karine must buy so that she has no food left in a sack at the end of a day?

C

5 Work out

a $1\frac{1}{2} \div \frac{3}{5}$ **b** $\frac{5}{8} \div 2\frac{2}{3}$

B

6 **a** Work out

i $4\frac{2}{3} \div 1\frac{1}{8}$ **ii** $4\frac{1}{6} \div 3\frac{3}{4}$

Write each answer in its simplest form.

AO2

b Use your answers to part **a** to work out $(4\frac{2}{3} \div 1\frac{1}{8}) - (4\frac{1}{6} \div 3\frac{3}{4})$.

B

7 Dom says, 'If I divide $6\frac{2}{3}$ by $4\frac{4}{9}$, the answer will be exactly $\frac{1}{3}$ of $4\frac{1}{2}$.'
Is he correct? Show workings to support your answer.

AO3

Links to:

Higher Student Book
Ch12, pp.177–189

Key Points

Expanding brackets D C

To expand brackets, you multiply each term inside the bracket by the term outside the bracket. For example, $3(2a + 7) = 6a + 21$ and $x(3x + 5) = 3x^2 + 5x$.

Adding and subtracting expressions with brackets D C

To add or subtract expressions with brackets, expand all the brackets first. Then collect like terms to simplify your answer.

Collecting like terms means adding all the terms in x together, adding all the terms in y together, etc.

Solving equations with brackets D C

To solve an equation with brackets, you usually expand the brackets first.

If there are any common factors on both sides of the equation, you can cancel them before expanding the brackets.

Factorising D C B

Factorising an algebraic expression is the opposite of expanding brackets.

Start by writing a common factor of both terms outside a bracket.
Then work out the terms inside the bracket.

factorising

$8t - 10 = 2(4t - 5)$

expanding

Expanding two brackets C B

To expand two brackets, you multiply each term in one bracket by each term in the other bracket.

Grid method

$(x + 2)(x + 5)$

$\times$	x	5
x	x^2	$5x$
2	$2x$	10

FOIL method

$(x + 2)(x + 5)$

Firsts: $x \times x = x^2$

Outers: $x \times 5 = 5x$

Inners: $2 \times x = 2x$

Lasts: $2 \times 5 = 10$

Then add the terms together and simplify.
$(x + 2)(x + 5) = x^2 + 5x + 2x + 10$
$= x^2 + 7x + 10$

Squaring a linear expression C B

To square an expression, write out the expression in brackets twice and expand.

For example, $(x + 4)^2 = (x + 4)(x + 4)$
$= x^2 + 8x + 16$

Identities C

An identity is a statement that is true for all values of x. For example, the statement $3(x + 2) \equiv 3x + 6$ is an identity.

12.1 Expanding brackets

1 Expand the following brackets.

   a $4(p + 2)$ **b** $5(6 - h)$ **c** $7(a + b)$

   d $3(2 + m + n)$ **e** $5(g + 5 - q)$ **f** $12(y - b - 9)$

2 Multiply out the brackets.

   a $5(2a + 4)$ **b** $3(3f - t)$ **c** $6(3d + h)$

   d $2(8g + 4r - 5)$ **e** $6(y^2 + 3y + 2)$ **f** $8(2e - 3d + 4f - 7)$

3 Show that $3(x - 2) + 15x \equiv 6(3x - 1)$.

4 Show that $5(4x - 3) + 3 \not\equiv 2(10x - 9)$.

$\not\equiv$ **means 'is not identically equal to'.**

5 Expand the following brackets.

   a $x(x + 3)$ **b** $y(y - 4)$ **c** $n(3n + 2)$

   d $5m(2m - 1)$ **e** $4t(2t + 4g)$ **f** $3p(5h - 3p)$

6 Expand the following brackets.

   a $x^2(x + 9)$ **b** $y(y^2 - 3)$ **c** $3z(2z - 5z^2)$

D

D

A02

D

C

7 **i** Write an expression for the area of each shape using brackets.
ii Expand the brackets.

> area of rectangle = length × width

a

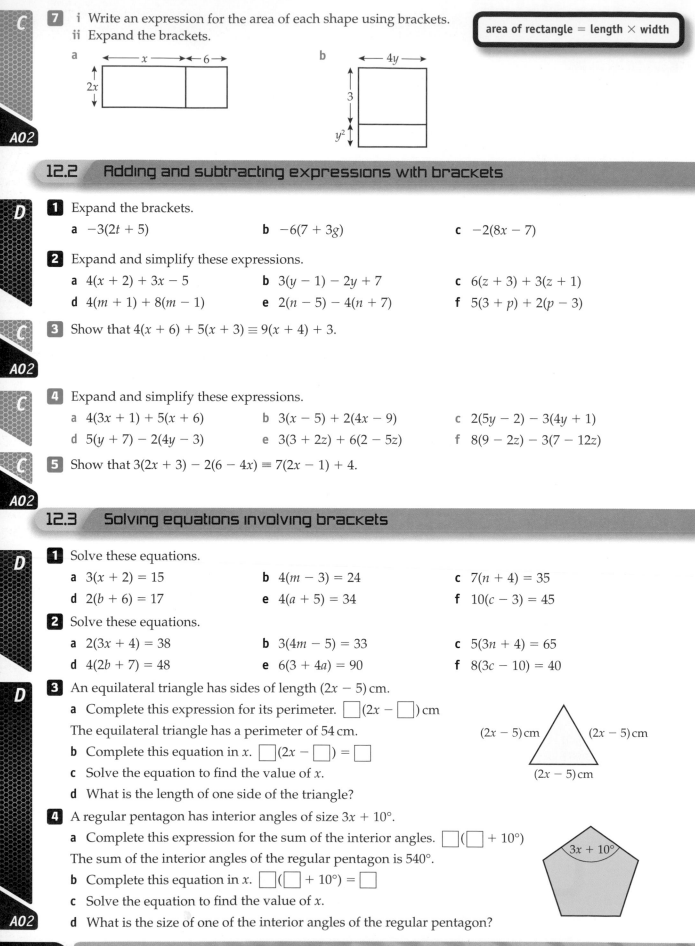

b

12.2 Adding and subtracting expressions with brackets

1 Expand the brackets.

    a $-3(2t + 5)$ **b** $-6(7 + 3g)$ **c** $-2(8x - 7)$

2 Expand and simplify these expressions.

    a $4(x + 2) + 3x - 5$ **b** $3(y - 1) - 2y + 7$ **c** $6(z + 3) + 3(z + 1)$

    d $4(m + 1) + 8(m - 1)$ **e** $2(n - 5) - 4(n + 7)$ **f** $5(3 + p) + 2(p - 3)$

3 Show that $4(x + 6) + 5(x + 3) \equiv 9(x + 4) + 3$.

4 Expand and simplify these expressions.

    a $4(3x + 1) + 5(x + 6)$ **b** $3(x - 5) + 2(4x - 9)$ **c** $2(5y - 2) - 3(4y + 1)$

    d $5(y + 7) - 2(4y - 3)$ **e** $3(3 + 2z) + 6(2 - 5z)$ **f** $8(9 - 2z) - 3(7 - 12z)$

5 Show that $3(2x + 3) - 2(6 - 4x) \equiv 7(2x - 1) + 4$.

12.3 Solving equations involving brackets

1 Solve these equations.

    a $3(x + 2) = 15$ **b** $4(m - 3) = 24$ **c** $7(n + 4) = 35$

    d $2(b + 6) = 17$ **e** $4(a + 5) = 34$ **f** $10(c - 3) = 45$

2 Solve these equations.

    a $2(3x + 4) = 38$ **b** $3(4m - 5) = 33$ **c** $5(3n + 4) = 65$

    d $4(2b + 7) = 48$ **e** $6(3 + 4a) = 90$ **f** $8(3c - 10) = 40$

3 An equilateral triangle has sides of length $(2x - 5)$ cm.

    a Complete this expression for its perimeter. $\square(2x - \square)$ cm

    The equilateral triangle has a perimeter of 54 cm.

    b Complete this equation in x. $\square(2x - \square) = \square$

    c Solve the equation to find the value of x.

    d What is the length of one side of the triangle?

4 A regular pentagon has interior angles of size $3x + 10°$.

    a Complete this expression for the sum of the interior angles. $\square(\square + 10°)$

    The sum of the interior angles of the regular pentagon is 540°.

    b Complete this equation in x. $\square(\square + 10°) = \square$

    c Solve the equation to find the value of x.

    d What is the size of one of the interior angles of the regular pentagon?

1 Copy and complete.

    a $5x + 10 = 5(\square + 2)$
    b $3v - 21 = 3(\square - 7)$
    c $3y + 15 = 3(y + \square)$

    d $4r - 48 = \square(r - 12)$
    e $2p - 18 = \square(p - 9)$
    f $6k + 36 = \square(k + \square)$

2 Factorise these expressions.

    a $2x + 12$
    b $3y - 12$
    c $4z + 24$

    d $5e + 35$
    e $32 + 8f$
    f $60 - 12g$

3 Factorise these expressions.

    a $y^2 + 4y$
    b $h^2 - 8h$
    c $2x + x^2$

4 Six of these cards show the numbers that are missing from the factorisations below.

    | 4 | 3 | 9 | 5 | 8 | 7 | 2 | 6 |

    $6x + 8 = \square(3x + \square)$ $5y - 15 = \square(y - \square)$ $m^2 + 8m = m(m + \square)$ $14 - 2t^2 = 2(\square - t^2)$

    What is the product of the two number cards that are not used in the factorisations?

5 Factorise these expressions.

    a $4y^2 + 12y$
    b $8xy - 16y^2$
    c $6p^2 + 9pq$

6 Factorise these expressions.

    a $6a^2b - 9ab^2$
    b $15xy^3 + 10y^2$
    c $16m^2n^2 - 20mn^3$

1 Expand and simplify these expressions.

    a $(x + 2)(x + 3)$
    b $(x + 3)(x - 2)$
    c $(x - 1)(x + 4)$

    d $(x + 3)(5 - x)$
    e $(4 - x)(x - 3)$
    f $(x + 6)(x - 6)$

    g $(x - 5)(x + 5)$
    h $(x + y)(x - y)$
    i $(x - c)(x + c)$

2 Show that $(x + 1)(x + 8) - (x + 2)(x + 4) \equiv 3x$.

3 Expand and simplify these expressions.

    a $(4a + 2)(3a + 5)$
    b $(6b + 1)(3b - 1)$
    c $(2c - 3)(5c - 2)$

4 Show that $(4x + 3)(6x - 2) \equiv 6(4x^2 + 2x - 1) - 2x$.

5 Expand and simplify.

    a $(x + 3)^2$
    b $(x - 6)^2$
    c $(4 - x)^2$

6 Expand and simplify.

    a $(3x - 1)^2$
    b $(2x + 5)^2$
    c $(4y + 2x)^2$

7 **a** Show that $(2x + 4)^2 \equiv 4(x + 2)^2$.   **b** Use $x = 5$ in part **a** to work out 14^2.

    c Work out 24^2 using this method.

Key Points

Multiplying decimals   **D**

To multiply decimals

1   Ignore the decimal points and just multiply the numbers.

2   Count the decimal places in the calculation.

3   Put this number of decimal places in the answer.

Dividing decimals   **D** **C**

You can divide a decimal by a whole number in the usual way.

If you are dividing by a decimal, first write it as a fraction, and convert the denominator to a whole number. Then divide in the usual way.

Converting decimals to fractions   **D**

You can use a place value diagram to convert a decimal to a fraction.

First write the decimal as tenths, hundredths, thousandths, …

Take the biggest denominator and put it on the bottom of a fraction. Put the decimal digits on the top of the fraction. Remember to give your answer in its simplest form.

Converting fractions to decimals   **D** **C**

To convert a fraction to a decimal, divide the numerator by the denominator.

Terminating decimals   **B**

Terminating decimals come to an end, for example, 0.6.

If the denominator of a fraction in its simplest form only has prime factors of 2 and/or 5, the fraction can be expressed as a terminating decimal.

Recurring decimals   **C** **B** **A**

Recurring decimals never come to an end, for example 0.333 … 'Recurring dots' are used to make the pattern clear, for example 0.$\dot{3}$. A dot over a digit shows that it recurs. Two dots show that a sequence of digits recurs.

If the denominator of a fraction in its simplest form has any prime factors other than 2 and 5, it will give a recurring decimal.

To convert a recurring decimal to a fraction

1   Write an equation, using x to represent the recurring decimal. For example, $x = 0.333 \ldots$

2   Multiply both sides by a power of ten to form a second equation.

3   Subtract the smaller equation from the larger. This leaves you with whole numbers only.

4   Solve the equation to find the value of x.

13.1   Multiplying and dividing decimals

D

1 Work out

   a 4.2×9 **b** 6.23×12 **c** 3.4×5.6 **d** 2.48×0.08

D

2   **a**   Work out   **i** 47.5×0.03 **ii** 475×0.003

    b   What do you notice about your answers to part **a**?

    c   Write down two more multiplications that have the same answers as part **a**.

3   Stewart is going to make a fruit salad.

    He buys 3 mangos. They cost him £1.38 each.

    a   What is the total cost of the mangos?

    He also buys 0.2 kg of blueberries. They cost him £13.25 per kg.

    b   What is the cost of the blueberries?

4   Serena buys 1.2 kg of cheese, priced at £8.45 per kg.

    Work out the cost of the cheese.

5   James saves £1 coins. He has saved £46.

    A £1 coin has a height of 3.15 mm.

    James puts all his coins in a single pile.

    How high is the pile of coins?

A02

    Give your answer in cm.

6 Work out

   a 6 ÷ 0.02   **b** 35 ÷ 0.007   **c** 2.98 ÷ 0.08

7 An office water dispenser contains 18.9 litres of water.

The cups provided hold 0.125 litres.

The water company claims the dispenser holds at least 150 cups of water.

Is this true? Show working to explain your answer.

8 Dylan is putting a wooden deck area in his back garden.

The deck area is 3.48 m wide.

Each decking plank is 0.12 m wide.

The decking planks come in packs of five.

How many packs must he buy?

0.12 m   3.48 m

9 Ahmed is buying tiles for a rectangular area of wall in his bathroom.

The area measures 2.75 m by 1.5 m.

He uses square tiles of side length 125 mm.

The tiles come in packs of 20. The price of each pack is £4.50.

He buys the smallest number of packs that he needs.

How much does Ahmed pay for the tiles?

13.2   Converting decimals and fractions

1 Convert each decimal to a fraction. Give the fraction in its lowest terms.

   a 0.4   **b** 0.9   **c** 0.01   **d** 0.35

   e 0.625   **f** 0.005   **g** 0.045   **h** 0.0006

2 Convert these to mixed numbers.

   a 4.2   **b** 12.6   **c** 8.45   **d** 9.15

3 Juan carried out a survey. He asked some people on which TV channel they preferred to watch the news. He found that a decimal fraction of 0.68 of the people preferred BBC1.

What fraction of the people preferred BBC1?

4 Convert each of these fractions to a decimal.

   a $\frac{3}{5}$ **b** $\frac{3}{8}$ **c** $\frac{4}{9}$ **d** $\frac{3}{11}$

   e $\frac{9}{50}$ **f** $\frac{3}{200}$ **g** $\frac{27}{500}$ **h** $\frac{17}{90}$

5 Write these fractions in order of size, smallest first.

   $\frac{37}{100}$ $\frac{4}{9}$ $\frac{3}{7}$ $\frac{1}{3}$ $\frac{2}{5}$

> Start by converting all the fractions into decimals.

6 Convert each of these fractions to a decimal.

   $\frac{1}{9}$ $\frac{1}{90}$ $\frac{1}{900}$ $\frac{1}{9000}$

What do you notice?

7 Convert each of these fractions to a decimal.

   $\frac{1}{14}$ $\frac{3}{14}$ $\frac{5}{14}$ $\frac{7}{14}$ $\frac{9}{14}$ $\frac{11}{14}$ $\frac{13}{14}$

What do you notice?

C

1 Convert each of these fractions to a decimal.

a $\frac{2}{9}$ b $\frac{4}{5}$ c $\frac{13}{20}$ d $\frac{2}{7}$

e $\frac{3}{25}$ f $\frac{19}{40}$ g $\frac{8}{9}$ h $\frac{13}{27}$

B

2 By looking at the denominators, predict which of these fractions will give terminating decimals and which will give recurring decimals.

$\frac{19}{20}, \frac{5}{6}, \frac{1}{5}, \frac{11}{14}, \frac{5}{18}, \frac{37}{250}, \frac{7}{24}, \frac{41}{72}, \frac{3}{125}, \frac{14}{15}$

Copy the table, and write your predictions in the table. The first one is done for you.

Terminating decimal	Recurring decimal
$\frac{19}{20}$	

B

3 a Copy and complete this table of recurring decimals.

Fraction	Recurring decimal	Number of digits in the recurring pattern
$\frac{1}{3}$	$0.\dot{3}$	1
$\frac{1}{7}$	$0.\dot{1}4285\dot{7}$	6
$\frac{1}{6}$		
$\frac{1}{9}$		
$\frac{1}{12}$		
$\frac{1}{13}$		

b Is the number of digits in any of the recurring patterns larger than the denominator?

c Is there a connection between the denominators of the fractions with one recurring digit?

d How many recurring digits are there in the decimals of fractions with an even-number denominator?

e Does the connection you found in part **d** work for all fractions with an even-number denominator? Can you find a fraction to prove it isn't always the case?

f From the table how many recurring digits are there in the decimals of fractions with a prime-number denominator?

g Does the connection you found in part **f** work for all fractions with a prime-number denominator? If not, find a fraction to prove it isn't always the case.

AO3

13.4   Converting recurring decimals to fractions

A

1 Convert each of these recurring decimals to a fraction in its simplest form.

a $0.\dot{5}$ b $0.\dot{3}\dot{6}$ c $0.4\dot{8}\dot{3}$

d $0.2\dot{4}$ e $0.7\dot{1}\dot{2}$ f $0.9\dot{1}2\dot{4}$

A

2 Sandeep says, 'I know that $\frac{1}{9}$ is $0.\dot{1}$, so this means that $\frac{1}{99}$ is $0.0\dot{1}$'

Alisha says, 'You're wrong, $\frac{1}{9}$ is $0.\dot{1}$, so this means that $\frac{1}{90}$ is $0.0\dot{1}$'

Who is correct? Show working to prove your answer.

AO2

Key Points

Equations with brackets D C

When you solve equations with brackets, you usually expand all the brackets first.

Equations with an unknown on both sides D C

To solve this type of equation you need to get the unknown on one side of the equals sign only. For example,

$$3x - 3 = 2x + 5$$
$$3x - 2x - 3 = 2x - 2x + 5$$
$$x - 3 = 5$$

Then solve the equation as normal.

Inequalities D C B

$x > 2$ is an inequality. It means that x must be greater than 2. $x \geq 2$ means that x must be greater than or equal to 2.

You can use the balance method to solve inequalities.

When you multiply both sides of the inequality by a negative number, you change the direction of the sign.

Equations with fractions C

When solving equations with fractions, eliminate the denominator by multiplying both sides of the equation by it.

When solving equations with two or more denominators, multiply by their lowest common multiple. This will eliminate the denominators and leave a much simpler equation.

Simultaneous equations B

To solve simultaneous equations you eliminate one of the unknowns using algebraic steps. You should then have a linear equation with one unknown, which you can solve.

14.1 Equations with brackets

1 Solve the following. D

a $5(a + 3) = 30$
b $3(x + 7) = 27$
c $4(c - 3) = 8$
d $10(x - 2) = 20$
e $2(e + 3) = -4$
f $5(3x + 2) = -20$
g $3(3g - 4) = 42$
h $20 = 4(3h - 7)$
i $125 = 5(20 + x)$

2 Solve the following. C

a $3(x + 4) + 4 = 25$
b $4(b + 3) + 2 + b = 24$
c $5(2x + 4) + 2x = 68$
d $7(d + 3) - 8 - 2d = 18$
e $4(4x + 10) - 6x = 20$
f $3(f - 3) + 4 + 2f = 20$
g $3(4x - 6) + 4 = -10$
h $5(4h - 3) - 2h = -1.5$
i $2(5 - 2x) + 7 + 8x = 57$
j $4(3j - 8) - 3 - 2j = -10$
k $2(3 - 2x) - x - 5 = 6$
l $10 + 3y + 2(3y + 4) = 45$

14.2 Equations with an unknown on both sides

1 Solve these equations. D

a $5u + 2 = 3u + 6$
b $4b + 3 = 3b + 6$
c $10c + 4 = 8c + 5$

2 Solve the following.

a $3x + 4 = 5 - x$
b $6x + 7 = 23 - 2x$
c $2x + 10 = -2 - 4x$

3 Solve the following. C

a $4x + 3 = 3(x + 2)$
b $3(4b + 2) = 10b + 16$
c $5(x + 2) = 3(6 + x)$
d $3(2x + 4) = 2(10x - 1)$
e $8(2x - 5) = 2(3x - 2)$
f $-2(3f - 2) = 11(2f + 8)$

4 In this cross the sum of the column is equal to the sum of the row.

a Use the cross to write an equation in x.

b Solve the equation to find the value of x.

	$x + 3$	
$4x + 6$	$2x + 4$	$8x - 2$
	$3x + 5$	

5 Work out the length and the width of this rectangle.

$$4y - 3$$

$x + 6$ ⬚ $3x + 2$

$$2y + 5$$

14.3 Equations with fractions

1 Solve the following equations by eliminating the denominator.

a $\dfrac{5x + 4}{7} = 2$

b $\dfrac{2x - 2}{5} = 2$

c $\dfrac{8x + 1}{3} = -5$

d $\dfrac{a + 3}{2} = \dfrac{2a + 1}{3}$

e $\dfrac{5b - 1}{7} = \dfrac{2b + 4}{5}$

f $\dfrac{c + 8}{3} = \dfrac{5c + 4}{6}$

2 Brett thinks of a number, adds 10 and divides the result by 4.

The answer to this is the same as when Brett starts with the same number, doubles it, adds 8 and divides the result by 6.

What number did Brett start with?

3 Jimmy has two function machines.

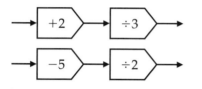

There is one number that when put into both function machines gives the same output number.

Find this number.

14.4 Inequalities

1 a Show $2 \leqslant x < 6$ on a number line.

b List all the whole-number values of x.

2 Solve each of the following inequalities.

a $7x < 21$

b $x - 7 > 21$

c $x + 3 \leqslant 1$

3 Solve each of the following inequalities.

a $2x + 3 \geqslant 17$

b $\dfrac{x}{4} - 10 \geqslant 1$

c $3(x - 4) < 6$

d $4(2x + 3) > 5x$

e $2x \leqslant 4x + 12$

f $4(2x + 1) < 44$

4 Solve each inequality. Show the solution on a number line.

a $9 < 3x \leqslant 15$

b $5x \geqslant 7x + 2$

5 Solve each inequality.

a $\dfrac{3x + 2}{2} \geqslant 4$

b $4(2x + 1) \geqslant 2(5 - 2x)$

6 List all integer solutions for the inequality $3 \leqslant 4(x + 3) < 22$.

14.5   Simultaneous equations

1 Solve each pair of simultaneous equations.

a $4x + y = 10$
  $4x - 4y = 0$

b $3x + y = 11$
  $5x - y = 13$

c $x + 3y = -5$
  $4x + 3y = -2$

2 Solve each pair of simultaneous equations.

a $5x + 3y = 14$
  $x + 2y = 7$

b $5x + 2y = 16$
  $4x + y = 11$

c $9x + 3y = 30$
  $5x - 2y = 2$

3 In September 2009, the total age of Amy and Dom was 64 years.
Amy is two years older than Dom.

a Write equations for the sum of their ages and the difference in their ages.

b Solve your equations simultaneously.

c In September 2009, how old were Amy and Dom?

4 The total wage bill for one day's work for 3 plumbers and 2 electricians is £864.
The total wage bill for one day's work for 5 plumbers and 7 electricians is £2144.
The plumbers and electricians work an 8-hour day.
What are the hourly rates of pay for a plumber and an electrician?

5 Penny has £20 000 to invest. She spends all the money on US dollars and euros.
Use d to represent the amount, in pounds, of dollars she buys.
Use e to represent the amount, in pounds, of euros she buys.

a Write an equation linking d and e and the total amount she invests.

Penny gets a 12% return on her dollar investment and a 4% return on her euro investment.
Altogether she gets £2000 in interest.

b Write an equation linking d and e and the total amount of interest she gets.

c Solve the equations to find out how many pounds Penny invested in each currency.

Key Points

Formulae written using letters and symbols **D**

You can use letters for the variables in a formula. For example, $p = hr + b$, where p is the pay, h is the hours worked, r is the rate of pay and b is the bonus.

Substitution **D C B**

Use the correct order of operations to help you do the calculations when you substitute values into an algebraic expression or formula.

Changing the subject of a formula **C B**

The subject of a formula only appears once, and only on its own side of the formula.

In the formula $v = u + at$, the variable v is the subject.

You can rearrange a formula to make a different variable the subject.

You can rearrange $v = u + at$ as $a = \dfrac{v - u}{t}$

15.1 Writing your own formulae

D

1 The price of straw is £S per bale and the price of hay is £H per bale.

Lawson buys 32 bales of straw and 65 bales of hay.

Write a formula for the total price, £T.

2 To cook baked potatoes in a microwave, Ruth allows 8 minutes per potato plus an extra 3 minutes.

Write a formula for the time, t minutes, it takes to cook p potatoes.

3 A square has a side length of $5x$.

a Write a formula for the perimeter, P, of this square.

b Write a formula for the area, A, of this square.

4 A triangle has a base length of $6x$ and a perpendicular height of $\frac{1}{2}x$.

Write a formula for the area, A, of this triangle.

5 A parallelogram has the dimensions shown.

a Write a formula for the perimeter, P, of this parallelogram.

b Write a formula for the area, A, of this parallelogram.

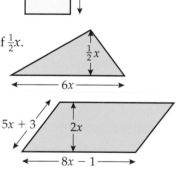

15.2 Substituting into expressions

D

1 Work out the value of these expressions when $a = 2$, $b = 4$ and $c = 6$.

a $3a^2 + 2$ **b** $2b^2 - 8$ **c** $c^2 + b$

d $8a + b^2$ **e** $a^3 + b + c$ **f** $b(c + 2)$

g $c(2a + b)$ **h** $\dfrac{3a + b}{2}$ **i** $\dfrac{c^2 - 3a}{10}$

2 Copy and complete this table.

x	0	1	2	3	4	5
$2x^2 + 3$	3			21		

3 Work out the value of these expressions when $v = 5$, $w = 7$, $x = 10$ and $y = -2$.

a $v(x - w)$ **b** $x^2 - vw$ **c** $\dfrac{2w + x}{2}$

d $\dfrac{4w - y}{x}$ **e** $v^2 + \dfrac{x}{y}$ **f** $\sqrt{v^2 - 12y}$

4 Work out the value of these expressions when $m = 1$, $n = 4$ and $p = -3$.

a $\dfrac{n^2 - 4p}{m^2 + n}$

b $\sqrt{6n - 3p + 3m}$

c $\dfrac{\sqrt{12n + 2n^2 + m}}{p}$

15.3 Substituting into formulae

1 The formula to work out an estimate of the shaded area, A, of this shape is $A = lw - 3r^2$.

a Work out an estimate of the shaded area when
  i $l = 8\,\text{cm}$, $w = 5\,\text{cm}$ and $r = 2\,\text{cm}$
  ii $l = 12\,\text{cm}$, $w = 8\,\text{cm}$ and $r = 3\,\text{cm}$.

b Work out an estimate of the length, l, when $A = 42\,\text{cm}^2$, $w = 9\,\text{cm}$ and $r = 4\,\text{cm}$.

c Work out an estimate of the width, w, when $A = 51\,\text{cm}^2$, $l = 9\,\text{cm}$ and $r = 2\,\text{cm}$.

2 Use the formula $s = \dfrac{t(u + v)}{2}$ to work out the value of s when

a $u = 5$, $v = 10$, $t = 3$ b $u = 15$, $v = 3$, $t = 5$.

3 An approximate value for the volume, V, of a sphere can be worked out using the formula
$V = \dfrac{88}{21}r^3$, where r is the radius of the sphere.

Work out an approximate value for the volume of a sphere with radius $5\,\text{cm}$.

Give your answer to the nearest cm^3.

4 Use the formula $s = \sqrt{\dfrac{v}{2}}$ to work out the value of s when

a $v = 72$ b $v = 288$.

5 Carlos makes resin paperweights in the shape of a cone.

To buy the correct amount of resin he needs to know the volume of one paperweight.

Volume of a cone $= \frac{1}{3}\pi r^2 h$, where r is the radius of the base and h is the height.

Find the volume of a paperweight that is $10\,\text{cm}$ tall and has a radius of $3.5\,\text{cm}$.

6 Use the formula $p = \sqrt{\dfrac{2r}{a}}$ to work out the value of p when

a $r = 18$ and $a = 4$ b $r = 2$ and $a = 16$.

7 Use the formula $P = \sqrt{\dfrac{2ab^2 + 3a^2b + (ab)^2}{3}}$ to work out the value of P when $a = 2$ and $b = 3$.

15.4 Changing the subject of a formula

1 Rearrange these formulae to make x the subject.

a $y = x + 5$ b $y = x - 9$ c $y = 5x$

d $y = wx$ e $y = 4x - 1$ f $y = 8x - 7$

g $y = 2x + 9p$ h $y = \frac{1}{2}x - 5t$ i $y = 3(x - 5)$

2 Rearrange these formulae to make x the subject.

a $4(x + y) = 4 + y$ b $y = \dfrac{x}{2} + r$ c $7w = \dfrac{4x}{5} + w$ d $y = \dfrac{x^2}{p} + m$

e $y = \sqrt{9 + x}$ f $y = 3\sqrt{x} + 5h$ g $y = 2\sqrt{\dfrac{x}{v}}$ h $y = \dfrac{3x^2 k}{8}$

3 A formula used in applied mathematics is $s = ut + \frac{1}{2}at^2$.

Rearrange the formula to make

a u the subject   b a the subject.

Key Points

Law of indices [C] [B]

To multiply powers of the same number you add the indices.

$x^n \times x^m = x^{n+m}$

To divide powers of the same number you subtract the indices.

$x^n \div x^m = x^{n-m}$

Powers of powers [A]

To calculate a power of a power you multiply the indices.

$(x^n)^m = x^{nm}$

Fractional and negative powers [C] [B] [A]

Any number to the power 1 is equal to the number itself.
For example, $6^1 = 6$, $x^1 = x$.

Any number to the power 0 is equal to 1.
For example, $6^0 = 1$, $x^0 = 1$.

A negative power is the reciprocal of the corresponding positive power.
For example, $9^{-4} = \frac{1}{9^4}$, $x^{-n} = \frac{1}{x^n}$.

If the index is a fraction then you can evaluate a number using roots.
For example $8^{\frac{1}{3}} = \sqrt[3]{8} = 2$, $x^{\frac{1}{n}} = \sqrt[n]{x}$.

Standard form [B]

Numbers in standard form have two parts. The first part is always a number greater than or equal to 1 and less than 10. The second part is a power of 10. You can use standard form to write very large or very small numbers.
For example, $360\,000 = 3.6 \times 10^5$, $0.0056 = 5.6 \times 10^{-3}$

Rational and irrational numbers [A]

Numbers that can be written in the form $\frac{a}{b}$ where a and b are both integer are called rational numbers.

Numbers that can't be written in this way are called irrational numbers.

Irrational numbers written as roots, such as $\sqrt{10}$, are called surds.

Simplifying surds [A] [A*]

$\sqrt{a} \times \sqrt{b} = \sqrt{ab}$

$\frac{\sqrt{a}}{\sqrt{b}} = \sqrt{\frac{a}{b}}$

You can simplify surds by looking for factors which are square numbers.

$\sqrt{8} = \sqrt{4 \times 2}$
$= \sqrt{4} \times \sqrt{2}$
$= 2\sqrt{2}$

You can simplify surds in fractions by rationalising the denominator.

$\frac{3}{\sqrt{7}} = \frac{3}{\sqrt{7}} \times \frac{\sqrt{7}}{\sqrt{7}}$

$= \frac{3\sqrt{7}}{\sqrt{7} \times \sqrt{7}}$

$= \frac{3\sqrt{7}}{7}$

16.1 Laws of indices

[C]

1 Write each of these expressions as a single power.

   a $2^4 \times 2^3$ **b** $5^3 \times 5^7$ **c** $3^4 \times 3^6 \times 3^3$

   d $\frac{6^6}{6^2}$ **e** $\frac{7^{10}}{7^7}$ **f** $8^{12} \div 8^2$

2 Use index laws to simplify these expressions.

   a $5^4 \div 5^3$ **b** $5^4 \div 5^4$ **c** $5^4 \div 5^5$

3 Write each of these expressions as a single power and work out its value.

   a $2^3 \times 2^2$ **b** $4^9 \div 4^7$ **c** $\frac{5^6}{5^4}$

[B]

4 Simplify each of these expressions and work out its value.

   a $\frac{3^2 \times 3^5}{3^4}$ **b** $\frac{8^3}{64}$ **c** $4^3 \times 4^5 \times 4^{-6}$

   d $\frac{5^2 \times 6^7}{5 \times 6^5}$ **e** $(2^2 \times 3^3) \times (2^3 \times 3^{-2})$ **f** $(5^4 \times 4^6) \times (5^{-2} \times 4^{-4})$

5 Simplify $(\sqrt{7})^2$.

6 Write each expression as a single power.

   a $(4^3)^2$ **b** $(5^{-1})^3$ **c** $(6^7)^{-2}$

7 Write each expression as a single power.

   a $\sqrt{4^{10}}$ **b** $\sqrt[3]{6^{15}}$ **c** $(\sqrt[4]{5})^{36}$

   d $\dfrac{9 \times 3^8}{(3^2)^3}$ **e** $\dfrac{\sqrt[5]{5^{15}} \times 5^4}{125}$ **f** $\dfrac{\sqrt{7^{20}}}{(7^3)^2}$

16.2 Fractional and negative powers

1 Evaluate

   a 4^{-1} **b** 8^0 **c** 3^{-2} **d** 7^1

2 Write $\dfrac{3^2 \times 2^3}{3^5 \times 2^2}$ as an exact fraction.

3 You are given that $3^7 \times 2^5 = 69\,984$ and $3^5 \times 2^3 = 1944$.

   a Write the value of $69\,984 \div 1944$ in index notation.

   b Work out $69\,984 \div 1944$.

4 John says, '$\frac{1}{3} \times \frac{1}{3} \times \frac{1}{3} \times \frac{1}{3} \times \frac{1}{3} \times \frac{1}{3} \times \frac{1}{3} = \frac{1}{3}^7$.'

   Jim says, '$\frac{1}{3} \times \frac{1}{3} \times \frac{1}{3} \times \frac{1}{3} \times \frac{1}{3} \times \frac{1}{3} \times \frac{1}{3} = 3^{-7}$.'

   Who is correct? Explain your answer.

5 Evaluate

   a $36^{\frac{1}{2}}$ **b** $49^{0.5} \times 2^3$ **c** $9^{\frac{1}{2}} \times 5^{-2}$

   d $8^{\frac{2}{3}}$ **e** $27^{\frac{4}{3}}$ **f** $100^{\frac{3}{2}}$

6 Work out

   a $81^{-\frac{1}{2}}$ **b** $16^{-\frac{3}{4}}$ **c** $64^{-\frac{2}{3}}$

16.3 Standard form

1 Write each of these numbers in standard form.

   a 450   **b** 8000   **c** 45 000 000   **d** 25.8

   e 0.056   **f** 0.000 067 8   **g** 0.000 09   **h** 0.2059

2 Write each of these as a decimal number.

   a 6.7×10^3 **b** 4.05×10^6 **c** 2×10^{-4} **d** 3.099×10^{-5}

3 The table shows the oil production of some countries.

Country	Oil production (barrels per day)
Zambia	1.5×10^2
USA	8.457×10^6
The Netherlands	8.895×10^6
Madagascar	9.2×10
Russia	9.98×10^6
Germany	1.481×10^5
Finland	8.951×10^3
India	8.8×10^5

Arrange the countries in order of oil production, starting with the largest.

4 The population of China in 2009 was estimated to be 1 338 612 968.

Write this number in standard form correct to three significant figures.

5 The unified atomic mass unit, used in science, has a value of 1.66×10^{-24} g, correct to three significant figures.

Write this number as a decimal number.

6 Work out these. Give your answers in standard form.

a $(4 \times 10^3) + (2 \times 10^3)$ b $(8 \times 10^5) + (6 \times 10^5)$ c $(5 \times 10^4) + (5 \times 10^5)$

d $(6 \times 10^5) - (2 \times 10^5)$ e $(5 \times 10^5) - (5 \times 10^4)$ f $(2 \times 10^5) - (6 \times 10^4)$

g $(4 \times 10^5) \times (2 \times 10^2)$ h $(3 \times 10^6) \times (4 \times 10^3)$ i $(8 \times 10^9) \div (4 \times 10^5)$

j $(1.5 \times 10^7) \div (3 \times 10^4)$ k $(9 \times 10^5) \times (1.1 \times 10^{-2})$ l $(6 \times 10^{-5}) \times (5 \times 10^{12})$

7 The population of the EU is approximately 5×10^8.

The EU has a total land area of approximately 4×10^6 km^2.

What is the population density (people/km^2) of the EU?

8 Approximately 50% of the population of the USA make up the USA labour force.

In 2009 the population of the USA was approximately 300 million, and the total value of USA exports was approximately 1.2×10^{12}.

Work out the approximate value of USA exports per person in the USA labour force.

16.4   Surds

1 Simplify these expressions.

a $\sqrt{5} \times \sqrt{7}$ b $\sqrt{2} \times \sqrt{3}$ c $\sqrt{18} \div \sqrt{3}$ d $\sqrt{21} \div \sqrt{7}$

2 Simplify, then evaluate these expressions.

a $\sqrt{2} \times \sqrt{8}$ b $\sqrt{2} \times \sqrt{50}$ c $\sqrt{24} \div \sqrt{6}$ d $\sqrt{75} \div \sqrt{3}$

3 Simplify these expressions.

a $3\sqrt{2} \times 5\sqrt{3}$ b $9\sqrt{5} \times 2\sqrt{2}$ c $20\sqrt{6} \div 5\sqrt{3}$ d $24\sqrt{12} \div 8\sqrt{6}$

4 Simplify, then evaluate these expressions.

a $2\sqrt{2} \times 3\sqrt{2}$ b $5\sqrt{3} \times 3\sqrt{12}$ c $12\sqrt{8} \div 4\sqrt{2}$ d $6\sqrt{48} \div 2\sqrt{3}$

5 Write each of these in the form $a\sqrt{b}$.

a $\sqrt{8}$ b $\sqrt{18}$ c $\sqrt{75}$ d $\sqrt{98}$

6 Simplify

a $\sqrt{18} + \sqrt{8}$ b $\sqrt{125} - \sqrt{20}$

7 By rationalising the denominator, simplify each of these expressions.

a $\dfrac{5}{\sqrt{3}}$ b $\dfrac{4}{5\sqrt{2}}$ c $\dfrac{5\sqrt{3}}{3\sqrt{5}}$ d $\dfrac{4\sqrt{32}}{\sqrt{2}}$

8 Work out the perimeter of a triangle with side lengths $\sqrt{75}$ cm, $\sqrt{48}$ cm and $\sqrt{27}$ cm.

9 Simplify

a $(1 + \sqrt{2})(3 + \sqrt{2})$ b $(3 - \sqrt{5})(4 + \sqrt{20})$ c $(3 + \sqrt{3})(3 - \sqrt{3})$ d $(4 + \sqrt{7})^2$

10 The area of a triangle is 30 cm^2.

The length of the base is $5\sqrt{3}$ cm. Work out the height of the triangle.

Key Points

Sequences [D]

A sequence is a list of numbers in a given order.

To find the next term in the sequence, look at the differences between consecutive terms.
The nth term of a sequence can be used to find any term in the sequence.

Finding the nth term of a linear sequence [C]

To find the nth term of a sequence, first look at the differences between consecutive terms.

Then compare the sequence to the multiples of the difference.

Finding the nth term of a quadratic sequence [C]

If the second row of differences are the same then the sequence is quadratic.

To find the general term compare the sequence to the square numbers (n^2).

Proof [D] [C] [B] [A]

A proof uses logical reasoning to show something is true.

Proof or verification? [C]

To verify means to check whether something is true by trying it out.

To prove means to show something is true through logical argument.

Disproof by counter-example [C]

A counter-example is an example which shows that a statement is false.

You can disprove a statement if you can find *just one* example that doesn't fit it.

Algebraic proof [B] [A] [A*]

When proving a statement algebraically you may need to use the following techniques.

- Expanding brackets
- Factorising
- Simplifying

17.1   Finding the nth term

1 The first four terms of a linear sequence are 9, 14, 19, 24.

   a Write down the next three terms.

   b Copy and complete the table.

	1st term	2nd term	3rd term	4th term
Sequence	9	14	19	24
Multiples of ...				

   c Use your table to find the nth term of the sequence.

2 Find the nth term of each sequence.

   a 7, 10, 13, 16, 19, ...   b 5, 7, 9, 11, 13, ...

   c −3, 1, 5, 9, 13, ...   d 22, 12, 2, −8, ...

3 The first four terms of a sequence are 3, 7, 11, 15.

   a Find the nth term of the sequence.

   b Use the nth term to find
     i the 25th term
     ii the 250th term.

4 Find the 25th term of the sequence 1, 6, 11, 16, ...

5 Find the 30th term of the sequence 30, 22, 14, 6, ...

[C]

[C]

[C]

[A02]

6 The first four terms of a sequence are 13, 7, 1, −5.

Find the term that is closest to −45.

7 A sequence begins 12, 19, 26, 33, ...

One of the terms in the sequence is 166. Which number term is this?

8 Here is a sequence: 3, 17, 31, 45, ...

a One of the terms in the sequence is 157. Which number term is this?

b Explain why 468 cannot be a term in this sequence.

17.2 Sequences of patterns

1 Here is the start of a sequence of patterns of dots.

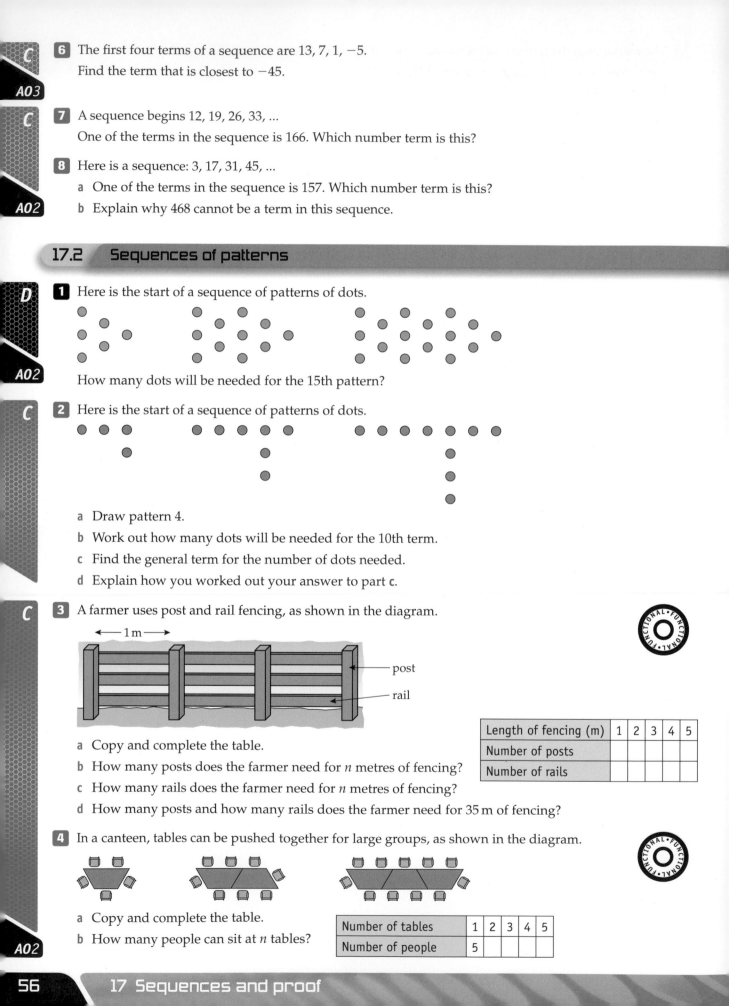

How many dots will be needed for the 15th pattern?

2 Here is the start of a sequence of patterns of dots.

a Draw pattern 4.

b Work out how many dots will be needed for the 10th term.

c Find the general term for the number of dots needed.

d Explain how you worked out your answer to part **c**.

3 A farmer uses post and rail fencing, as shown in the diagram.

a Copy and complete the table.

b How many posts does the farmer need for n metres of fencing?

c How many rails does the farmer need for n metres of fencing?

d How many posts and how many rails does the farmer need for 35 m of fencing?

Length of fencing (m)	1	2	3	4	5
Number of posts					
Number of rails					

4 In a canteen, tables can be pushed together for large groups, as shown in the diagram.

a Copy and complete the table.

b How many people can sit at n tables?

Number of tables	1	2	3	4	5
Number of people	5				

5 The manager of the canteen in Q4 has 72 chairs altogether.

He makes a row of as many full tables as he can. How many chairs will he have left over?

6 The diagrams show a sequence of cuboids.

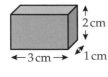 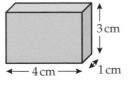 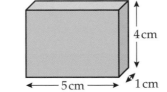

a Work out the volume of cuboid 4.

b The diagram shows the nth cuboid in the sequence. Write down an expression for
    i the height of cuboid n
    ii the length of cuboid n
    iii the depth of cuboid n
    iv the volume of cuboid n.

c What is the volume of the 11th cuboid in the sequence?

17.3   Quadratic sequences

1 Find the next three terms in the sequence 4, 7, 12, 19, ...

2 The general term of a sequence is $n^2 + 9$.

  a Work out the first three terms of the sequence.

  b What is the 12th term of the sequence?

3 The nth term of a sequence is $3n^2$.

  a Work out the first three terms of the sequence.

  b What is the 10th term of the sequence?

4 A sequence has general term $2n^2 - 1$.

Is 135 a number in the sequence? Explain your answer.

5 Copy and complete this quadratic sequence.

4, 10, ☐, ☐, 52, 74, 100, ...

6 Find the nth term of each of the following sequences, by comparing them with the square numbers.

  a 6, 9, 14, 21, ...   **b** 0, 3, 8, 15, ...   **c** 26, 29, 34, 41, ...

  d 2, 8, 18, 32, ...   **e** 6, 12, 22, 36, ...   **f** −2, 4, 14, 28, ...

7 Find the 10th term of each of the sequences in Q6.

17.4   Proof or verification?

1 n is an odd number larger than 1.

Explain why $n^2 - 2$ is always an odd number.

2 The sum of four consecutive integers is always an even number.
Show that this is true for four consecutive integers of your choice.

3 If x is odd and y is even, $x^2 + y^2$ is odd. Verify that this statement is true if $x = 3$ and $y = 4$. Do you think the statement will always be true? Explain your answer.

4 Given that x and y are prime numbers bigger than 2, show that $x + y$ is even.

5 Show that the product of two even numbers is always a multiple of 4.

17.5 Using counter-examples

1 Give a counter-example to show that each of these statements is false.

  a When you find a percentage of an amount, the answer is always smaller than the number you started with.

  b When you find a fraction of a fraction, the answer is always smaller than the fraction you started with.

2 Charlie says, 'I am thinking of a number. When I round my number to the nearest 10, I get an answer of 460.'

Alfie says that Charlie's number must be bigger than 459.

Give a counter-example to show that Alfie is wrong.

3 Li says, 'The sum of three consecutive square numbers is always even.'

Show that Li is wrong.

4 Alexi says, 'If x and y are integers, then $xy - 2$ is always even.'

Show that Alexi is wrong.

5 Brian says, 'If x is an integer, then $2x^3 + 1$ is always even.'

Show that Brian is wrong.

6 Show that the statement $\sqrt[3]{x} < x$ is not true for all values of x.

17.6 Proof using algebra

1 When n is an odd number larger than 1, prove that $n^2 - 2$ is always an odd number.

> **Remember to use these facts:**
> - A number of the form $2k$ is even.
> - A number of the form $2k + 1$ is odd.

2 Prove that the sum of four consecutive integers is always an even number.

3 Prove that the product of two consecutive odd numbers is always 1 less than a multiple of 4.

4 Prove that $(3n - 1)^2 \equiv (n + 1)^2 + 8n(n - 1)$.

5 Given that x is odd and y is even, prove that $x^2 + y^2$ is odd.

6 A, B and C are three consecutive odd numbers.

Prove that $A^2 + B^2 - C^2 \equiv B \times (C - 10)$.

Key Points

Percentage increase and decrease **D**

Method A

1 Work out the value of the increase (or decrease).

2 Add it to (or subtract it from) the original amount.

Method B

1 Add the percentage increase to 100%
   (or subtract the percentage decrease from 100%).

2 Convert this percentage to a decimal.

3 Multiply it by the original amount.

Calculations involving VAT **D**

VAT stands for Value Added Tax. It is a tax that is added to the price of most items in shops and to many other services.

VAT is calculated as a percentage. Generally it is 17.5% in the UK.

Percentage profit or loss **C**

$$\text{percentage profit} = \frac{\text{actual profit}}{\text{cost price}} \times 100\%$$

$$\text{percentage loss} = \frac{\text{actual loss}}{\text{cost price}} \times 100\%$$

where actual profit (or loss) is the difference between the cost price and the selling price.

Repeated percentage change **C**

Generally when you invest money the interest is calculated on the amount invested in the first place plus any interest already received. This is known as compound interest.

1 Add the rate of interest to 100%.

2 Convert this percentage to a decimal.

3 Multiply the original amount by the multiplier repeatedly for each year invested.

You can also use this method to work out a repeated percentage loss or depreciation, except that to find the multiplier you must first subtract the percentage from 100%.

Finding the original quantity **B**

To work out the original quantity when you are given the quantity after a percentage increase or decrease, use one of these methods.

Method A

1 Work out what percentage the figure you are given represents.

2 Divide by this percentage to find 1%.

3 Multiply by 100 to get the 100% figure.

Method B

1 Work out what percentage the figure you are given represents.

2 Divide by 100 to find the multiplier.

3 Divide the figure you are given by the multiplier.

18.1 Percentage increase and decrease

1 **a** Increase £920 by 10%. **b** Decrease 60 km by 5%.
   c Increase 64 mm by 2%. **d** Decrease $60 by 9%.

2 Salina books a holiday to France.
The price of the holiday is £680. She pays an extra 15% single supplement.
What is the total price of her holiday?

3 Salina is going on holiday by plane.
She books her car into the airport car park.
The normal price is £52. She pays online and gets an 8% discount.
How much does she pay for the car park?

4 A wet-suit, priced at £130, is reduced by 25% in a sale.
After three weeks the wet-suit still hasn't been sold, so the shop reduces the price by a further 10%.
What is the final sale price of the wet-suit?

> The second reduction is 10% of the first sale price, not the original price.

D

D

AO2

5 Work out the total price of

   a a digital camera priced at £120 + 17.5% VAT

   b a sat-nav priced at £166 + 17.5% VAT

   c an oil fuel bill of £282 + 5% VAT.

6 Six friends go out for a meal.

   The restaurant bill is £156 + 17.5% VAT.

   a What is the total bill?

   b The friends share the bill equally. How much do they each pay?

18.2   Percentage profit or loss

C

1 Kiros buys a sculpture for £135 and sells it for £162.

   What is his percentage profit?

2 Dahlia buys a narrow boat for £64 500.

   She sells it five years later for £51 600.

   What is her percentage loss?

3 Sue sold an antique table for £132.

   She had paid £80 for it.

   What was her percentage profit?

4 Ellen bought a games console for £340.

   She later sold it for £238.

   What was her percentage loss?

C

5 Lars buys vases for £19 and sells them for £25.

   Krister buys vases for £15 and sells them for £21.

   Who makes the larger percentage profit?

6 Rasine bought a pressure washer for £120. She sold it one year later for £54.

   Misha bought a pressure washer for £138. He sold it two years later for £58.

A02   Who made the larger percentage loss?

18.3   Repeated percentage change

C

1 Tyler invests £2000 at a compound interest rate of 3% per annum.

   How much will he have at the end of three years?

2 Christos invests £1800 at a compound interest rate of 4% per annum.

   How much will he have at the end of three years?

3 The number of badgers in one area of the UK is increasing by 6% each year.

   In this particular area, there are estimated to be 400 badgers.

   Estimate the number of badgers in this area in two years' time.

4 The value of a sailing dinghy depreciates by 10% each year.

   Hazel buys a sailing dinghy for £2300. How much will it be worth after three years?

5 The value of a jet ski depreciates by 15% each year.

Hadrian buys a jet ski for £9800. How much will it be worth after four years?

6 At the start of the year, 200 people go to the Star bingo hall. The number of people going to the Star bingo hall is going down at a rate of 2% each week.

At the start of the year, 230 people go to the Bright bingo hall. The number of people going to the Bright bingo hall is going down at a rate of 5% each week.

After four weeks, which bingo hall has more people?

7 Grassholm Island in Pembrokeshire has one of the largest gannet colonies in the world.

In 2009, there were approximately 37 000 breeding pairs.

The number of gannets is increasing at an average rate of 2% per annum.

In which year will the number of breeding pairs be expected to reach 40 000?

18.4 Reverse percentages

1 Anders has an antique watch valued at £1000.

This is 25% more than he paid for it. How much did he pay for the watch?

2 Jana buys pet insurance for £46.

This price includes an 8% discount for buying online. What is the price of the insurance without the discount?

3 A running machine is in a sale.

What was the price of the running machine before the sale?

SALE! 15% off Running machine Now only **£782**

4 Issay checks his savings account.

He has £2800 in his account, which is 12% more than he started with.

How much money did he start with in his account?

5 Ted buys a house for £138 000.

He says, 'Last year, house prices rose by 15%. If I'd bought the house last year I would have saved £20 700.'

Is he correct? Show working to support your answer.

6 Morgen bought some shares two years ago.

Her shares have increased in value by 6% per annum. They are now worth £2809.

What was the value of the shares when Morgen bought them?

Links to:
Higher Student Book
Ch19, pp.274–296

Key Points

Mid-point of a line segment   **D** **C**

Mid-point $(x, y) = \left(\dfrac{x_1 + x_2}{2}, \dfrac{y_1 + y_2}{2}\right)$

where (x_1, y_1) and (x_2, y_2) are the coordinates of the end-points.

Straight-line graphs   **D** **C** **B** **A**

Straight-line graphs have equations of the form $y = mx + c$, where m is the gradient and c is the y-intercept.

The gradient of a straight line passing through two points $A(x_1, y_1)$ and $B(x_2, y_2)$ is

gradient, $m = \dfrac{\text{change in } y}{\text{change in } x}$

$\qquad = \dfrac{y_2 - y_1}{x_2 - x_1}$

Parallel lines have the same gradient.

A line that is perpendicular to a line with gradient m has gradient $-\dfrac{1}{m}$.

Simultaneous equations   **B**

You can solve a pair of simultaneous equations by drawing their graphs on the same set of axes.

The point on the graph where the two lines intersect is their solution.

Inequalities   **B**

Inequalities can be shown as a shaded region on a graph.

For the inequalities $\leqslant$ and $\geqslant$, the boundary is a solid line.

For the inequalities $<$ and $>$, the boundary is a dashed line.

Graphs describing journeys   **D** **C** **A**

A distance–time graph represents a journey. The x-axis (horizontal) represents the time taken. The y-axis (vertical) represents the distance from the starting point.

The gradient of a distance–time graph represents speed.

You can work out the average speed of a journey using

average speed $= \dfrac{\text{total distance}}{\text{total time}}$

Velocity is a measure of speed and direction.

On a velocity–time graph, the x-axis represents time and the y-axis represents velocity.

A horizontal line represents constant velocity.

The gradient of a velocity–time graph represents acceleration.

acceleration $= \dfrac{\text{change in velocity}}{\text{time}}$

A negative value represents deceleration.

The area under a velocity–time graph represents the distance travelled.

19.1   Mid-point of a line segment

D

1 For each line segment
   a write down the coordinates of the end-points
   b work out the coordinates of the mid-point.

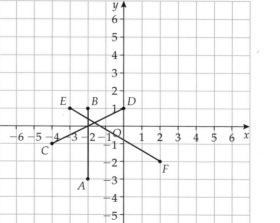

2 Work out the mid-points of these line segments.

    a *GH*: $G(-3, -4)$ and $H(0, 2)$

    b *IJ*: $I(7, 2)$ and $J(-1, -3)$

    c *KL*: $K(-3, 2)$ and $L(6, -2)$

C

3 *ABCDEF* is a shape with coordinates $A(-3, 2)$, $B(3, 2)$, $C(1, 0)$, $D(3, -2)$, $E(-3, -2)$ $F(-1, 0)$.

    a Work out the coordinates of the mid-point of the side *AB*.

    b Work out the coordinates of the mid-point of the side *BC*.

    c Work out the coordinates of the mid-point of the side *DE*.

    d Work out the coordinates of the mid-point of the side *AF*.

    e What shape do you get if you join the mid-points of sides *AB*, *BC*, *DE* and *AF*?

C

AO2

4 The point *G* has coordinates $(-3, 4)$.

The mid-point of the line segment *GH* has coordinates $(-1\frac{1}{2}, \frac{1}{2})$.

Work out the coordinates of the point *H*.

C

AO3

19.2   Plotting straight-line graphs

1 Draw the graph of $y = 3x + 1$ for $-3 \leqslant x \leqslant 3$.

> **Start by drawing a table of values from $x = -3$ to $x = 3$ and work out the y-coordinate that goes with each x-coordinate.**

D

2 **a** Copy and complete this table of values for $y = 3 - \frac{1}{2}x$.

    b Draw the graph of $y = 3 - \frac{1}{2}x$.

x	-2	-1	0	1	2
y		$3\frac{1}{2}$			2

    c Draw the line $x = 2$ on your graph.

C is the point where the two lines cross.

    d Mark the point *C* and write down its coordinates.

D

3 **a** Draw the lines $y = 2x + 1$ and $y = x - 3$ on the same graph.

    b How can you tell which is the steeper line from the equations?

    c By looking at the equations, how can you tell where each line intercepts the y-axis?

AO2

4 Jane says, 'The lines $y = 2x + 4$ and $x = -2$ cross at the point $(-2, -1)$.'

Is Jane's statement correct? Show working to support your answer.

D

AO3

5 **a** Copy and complete this table of values for $x + 3y = 9$.

    b Draw the graph of $x + 3y = 9$.

x	0	
y		0

C

6 Draw the graph of $4y + 5x = 20$.

> **Substitute $x = 0$, then $y = 0$, into the equation.**

C

AO2

19.3   Equations of straight-line graphs

1 Write down the gradient of these straight lines.

    a $y = 3x + 1$ **b** $y = 6 + \frac{1}{2}x$ **c** $y = -2x - 5$

C

2 Which of these straight lines are parallel to $y = -3x + 9$?

    A $y = -3x - 1$ **B** $y = 2 - 3x$ **C** $y = 3x - 9$

3 Write down the y-intercepts of these lines.

a $y = 5x + 2$ b $y = 1\frac{1}{2} + \frac{1}{2}x$ c $y = 2x - 4\frac{1}{2}$

4 Without plotting these straight lines, identify the ones parallel to the line $y = 2x - 5$.

A $2y = 4x + 7$ **B** $4y - 8x = 12$ **C** $3y + 6x = 9$

D $6y = 12x - 8$ **E** $2x = 13 + y$ **F** $2\frac{1}{2}x = 5y + 1$

5 Work out the gradient and intercept of each line.

a $3y = 9x - 15$ b $y + 4 = 2x$ c $5y - 25x = 35$

6 Work out the gradient of the line joining the points $(1, 0)$ and $(3, 4)$.

7 A line has gradient 3 and passes through the point $(0, 2)$.

Work out the equation of the line.

8 A line passes through the points $(-4, 0)$ and $(2, 3)$.

Work out

a the gradient of the line

b the equation of the line.

9 The line segment AB has end-points $A(4, 2)$ and $B(-2, -1)$.

Find the equation of the line parallel to AB and passing through the point $(2, -2)$.

> **When two lines are parallel, their gradients are equal.**

10 Write the gradients of the lines that are perpendicular to the lines with the following gradients.

a 3   b $\frac{1}{5}$ c -6 d $2\frac{1}{2}$

> **When two lines are perpendicular, the product of their gradients is -1.**

11 Find the equation of the line perpendicular to $y = 3x + 1$ that passes through the point $(1, 0)$.

12 To avoid being trapped, a video game character must move along the perpendicular bisector of the line segment joining the points $(-2, 2)$ and $(4, 8)$.

Find the equation of the line it must move along to avoid being trapped.

19.4   Using graphs to solve simultaneous equations

1 Solve each pair of simultaneous equations graphically.

a $2x + y = 8$
   $x + 2y = 7$

b $3x + y = 18$
   $4x - y = 10$

2 Use a graphical method to show why the following simultaneous equations cannot be solved.

$2x + y = 6$
$2y = 6 - 4x$

3 Josh starts work at a café.

This is the 'Specials' menu board.

Two of the prices have accidentally been rubbed out.

Josh knows that one group of people ordered 3 lasagnes and 2 beef pies and it cost them £48.

Another group of people ordered 2 lasagnes and 1 beef pie and it cost them £28.

Josh writes down these two equations.

$3x + 2y = 48$

$2x + y = 28$

a Use a graphical method to solve the simultaneous equations.

b What is the price of a lasagne?

c What is the price of a beef pie?

Specials
Lasagne	£●
Curry & chips	£9
Fish & chips	£11
Beef pie	£●
Vegetable risotto	£8

AO2

19.5 Graphical inequalities

1 Use inequalities to describe the shaded regions on these graphs.

a
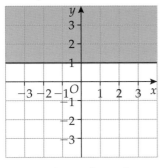

b

2 Draw graphs to show the region that satisfies each inequality.

a $x \leqslant -2$ **b** $y > -3$ **c** $y \geqslant 2x + 1$ **d** $y < -x$

3 Sketch the region defined by these three inequalities.

$x > 1$ $y > -3$ $2x + y \leqslant 4$

Mark the region with an 'R'.

4 Write down the three inequalities which together describe the shaded region on this graph.

D

1 Sam is driving from Edinburgh to Aberdeen for an interview.

She sets off at 8 am and travels 90 km in the first hour.

She travels the next 60 km in half an hour. She then stops for a 20-minute break.

The remaining 50 km takes her 20 minutes. Her interview takes 50 minutes.

She then drives straight home without stopping. The drive home takes her $2\frac{1}{2}$ hours.

a Draw a distance–time graph for Sam's journey.

b What time does she arrive in Aberdeen?

c What time does she arrive back in Edinburgh?

d During which part of the journey was Sam travelling the fastest?

e What was her speed during the fastest part of the journey?

f What was her average speed for the journey to Aberdeen?

g What was her average speed for the journey home to Edinburgh?

C

2 Rob is training for a fun run.

Each evening he goes for a run to the park and back.

He leaves his house at 6 pm.

Here is a distance–time graph of his training run one evening.

During this run he stopped to chat with a friend, and bought a paper on the way home.

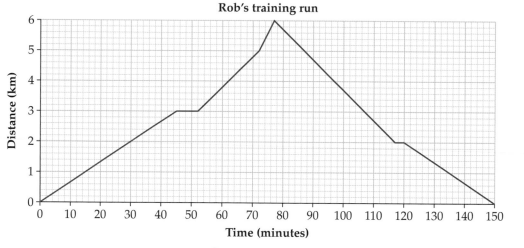

a How far did Rob run in the first $\frac{3}{4}$ hour?

b How long did he stop to talk to his friend?

c What time did Rob get to the paper shop?

d Work out the speed Rob was running during the fastest section of his run.

e Work out Rob's average speed for the whole training run.

A

3 The diagram shows a velocity–time graph for a short car journey.

Use the diagram to work out

a the acceleration in the first 30 seconds

b the deceleration in the last 50 seconds

c the total distance travelled.

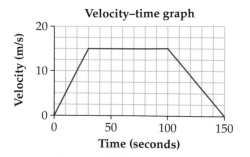

4 Water is poured at a steady rate into these containers.

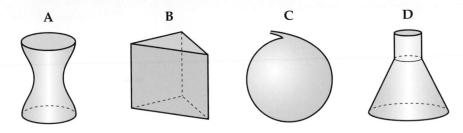

A   B   C   D

The depth of water in the containers is measured over time and graphs are plotted.

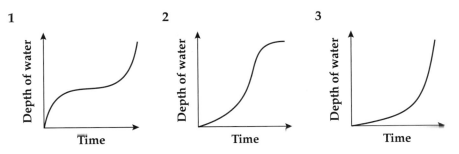

1   2   3

a Match the containers to the graphs.

b One container has not been matched. Which one is it?

c Sketch a graph for this container.

5 A water tank holds 100 litres.

Shen empties the water tank in three stages.
    Stage 1: 40 litres at 20 litres per minute
    Stage 2: 36 litres at 12 litres per minute
    Stage 3: 24 litres at 8 litres per minute

He then refills the tank at a steady rate of 25 litres per minute.

Draw a graph to show this information.

6 The graph shows an 800 m race between Alice and Betty.

Describe what happens in the race.

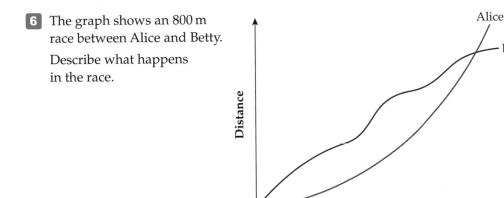

A03

Key Points

Difference of two squares [B] [A]

An expression of the form $x^2 - b^2$, where x and b are numbers or algebraic terms, is called the difference of two squares. In general, $x^2 - b^2 = b^2(x - b)(x + b)$.

Factorising quadratic expressions [B] [A] [A*]

To factorise an expression of the form $x^2 + bx + c$ you must find two numbers whose product is c and sum is b.

To factorise an expression of the form $ax^2 + bx + c$ you must first consider the factors of the coefficient of x^2 and then the other terms.

Solving quadratic equations [B] [A] [A*]

You can solve quadratic equations by

• **Rearranging**

Rearrange the equation to make the unknown the subject.

• **Factorising**

Rearrange the equation so all the terms are on one side, then factorise it. This way one of the pair of brackets must be equal to zero.

• **Using the quadratic formula**

The solution to the quadratic equation $ax^2 + bx + c = 0$, when $a \neq 0$, is

$$x = \frac{-b \pm \sqrt{b^2 - 4ac}}{2a}$$

• **Completing the square**

First write the equation in the form $(x + b)^2 + c = 0$, then rearrange to find the exact value of x.

The discriminant [A*]

The discriminant is the expression $b^2 - 4ac$ under the square root in the quadratic formula.

• If $b^2 - 4ac > 0$, there are two distinct solutions to the quadratic equation.

• If $b^2 - 4ac < 0$, there are no real solutions to the quadratic equation.

• If $b^2 - 4ac = 0$, there is one solution (sometimes called a repeated root).

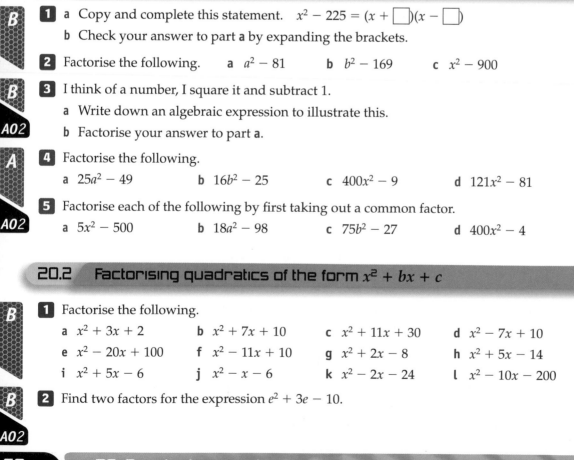

20.1 Factorising the difference of two squares

[B]

1 **a** Copy and complete this statement. $x^2 - 225 = (x + \square)(x - \square)$

b Check your answer to part **a** by expanding the brackets.

2 Factorise the following. **a** $a^2 - 81$ **b** $b^2 - 169$ **c** $x^2 - 900$

[B]

[A02]

3 I think of a number, I square it and subtract 1.

a Write down an algebraic expression to illustrate this.

b Factorise your answer to part **a**.

[A]

4 Factorise the following.

a $25a^2 - 49$ **b** $16b^2 - 25$ **c** $400x^2 - 9$ **d** $121x^2 - 81$

[A02]

5 Factorise each of the following by first taking out a common factor.

a $5x^2 - 500$ **b** $18a^2 - 98$ **c** $75b^2 - 27$ **d** $400x^2 - 4$

20.2 Factorising quadratics of the form $x^2 + bx + c$

[B]

1 Factorise the following.

a $x^2 + 3x + 2$ **b** $x^2 + 7x + 10$ **c** $x^2 + 11x + 30$ **d** $x^2 - 7x + 10$

e $x^2 - 20x + 100$ **f** $x^2 - 11x + 10$ **g** $x^2 + 2x - 8$ **h** $x^2 + 5x - 14$

i $x^2 + 5x - 6$ **j** $x^2 - x - 6$ **k** $x^2 - 2x - 24$ **l** $x^2 - 10x - 200$

[B]

2 Find two factors for the expression $e^2 + 3e - 10$.

[A02]

1 Solve these equations.

    a $x^2 = 400$ **b** $x^2 - 7 = 42$ **c** $3x^2 = 27$ **d** $\dfrac{x^2}{2.25} = 16$

B

2 Solve these equations by rearranging.

    a $3x^2 - 12 = 63$ **b** $2x^2 = 7x^2 - 80$ **c** $122 - 4t^2 = 86$

3 Find the roots of

    a $3(x + 1)^2 = 48$ **b** $(x + 2)^2 - 12 = 37$ **c** $\dfrac{(x - 3)^2}{4} = 1$

4 A laser etches a rectangle onto the side of a diamond.

The length of the rectangle is four times its width.

The area of the rectangle is $0.0064\,\text{cm}^2$.

    a Using x for the width of the rectangle, form and solve an equation.

    b What is the length of the rectangle in mm?

B
AO2

5 Solve the following quadratic equations by factorising.

    a $x^2 + 4x = 0$ **b** $b^2 - 5b = 0$ **c** $5x^2 + 15x = 0$

    d $2x^2 + 12x = 0$ **e** $3b^2 - b = 0$ **f** $4x = 8x^2$

B

6 Last year a farmer put a fence around one of her fields.

She remembers that the length of the field is three times the width.
She also knows that the field has an area of $67\,500\,\text{m}^2$.
Unfortunately she can't remember the dimensions of the field.

Form and solve a quadratic equation to work out the dimensions of the field.

B

7 The product of two consecutive even numbers is 288.

Form and solve a quadratic equation to find the two numbers.

AO3

1 Factorise each quadratic expression.

    a $3x^2 + 11x + 6$ **b** $5x^2 - 46x + 9$ **c** $7x^2 - 13x - 2$

A

2 Factorise each quadratic expression.

    a $4x^2 + 16x + 15$ **b** $8x^2 - 34x + 21$ **c** $6x^2 - x - 15$

3 Factorise each quadratic expression. Start by taking out a common factor.

    a $2x^2 + 14x + 24$ **b** $2x^2 + 20x + 42$ **c** $15x^2 + 50x + 40$

4 Solve the following for x. Leave your answers as fractions where necessary.

    a $2x^2 + 3x + 1 = 0$ **b** $3x^2 - 5x - 2 = 0$ **c** $4x^2 - 9x - 9 = 0$

    d $5x^2 = -2 - 11x$ **e** $x + 15 = 6x^2$ **f** $7x^2 - 2 = 13x$

5 **a** Write down an algebraic expression for the area of the rectangle.

    The area of the rectangle is $119\,\text{cm}^2$.

    b Work out the integer value of x.

Diagram: rectangle with width $3x + 2$ and height $2x - 3$.

A
AO2

6 I am a negative number.

Three times my square is equal to my value added to 80.

What number am I?

7 Next year Ian will be nine times the age of his son Joe.

Let x represent Joe's age next year.

a Write down an algebraic expression for
   i Ian's age next year
   ii Joe's age this year
   iii Ian's age this year.

The product of their ages this year is 176.

b Form and solve an equation to work out Joe's age next year.

c How old is Ian this year?

20.5   Using the quadratic formula

1 Use the quadratic formula to solve the following. Leave your answers in surd form.

a $x^2 - 6x - 1 = 0$ b $2x^2 + 6x + 3 = 0$ c $3x^2 + 8x - 6 = 0$

d $5x^2 = 5x - 1$ e $7 + 11x = 6x^2$ f $7x^2 + 4x = 29$

2 For each of these quadratic equations, decide if there are zero, one or two solutions.

a $2x^2 - 15x + 18 = 0$ b $x^2 + x - 1 = 0$ c $3x^2 + 7x - 8 = 0$

d $3x^2 + 6x + 3 = 0$ e $7x = 5x^2 + 3$ f $(2x + 4)^2 = 6x + 10$

g $x + 8 = -\dfrac{16}{x}$ h $\dfrac{3}{x + 2} = 4x$ i $\dfrac{10}{(x + 2)(x - 3)} = 1$

20.6   Completing the square

1 Write each expression in completed square form.

a $x^2 + 6x - 1$ b $x^2 + 4x - 3$ c $x^2 - 12x + 3$

2 Write each algebraic expression in the form $(x + p)^2 + q$, giving the values of p and q.

a $x^2 + 4x - 1$ b $x^2 - 8x + 9$ c $x^2 - 6x - 4$

3 Solve the following quadratic equations by completing the square.

Give your answers both in surd form and to two decimal places.

a $x^2 - 8x + 2 = 0$ b $2x^2 - 3x - 4 = 0$ c $3x^2 - 6x + 1 = 0$

d $3x^2 = 1 + 6x$ e $(2x + 2)^2 = 2x^2 + 11$ f $\dfrac{7 - 2x}{(4x + 1)(x - 1)} = 1$

Links to:
Higher Student Book
Ch21, pp.316–329

Key Points

Simultaneous equations: one linear, one quadratic

To solve simultaneous equations, where one is linear and the other is quadratic, you need to use the method of substitution.

Changing the subject of a formula [A] [A*]

To change the subject of a formula, use the same methods as for solving equations.

Algebraic fractions

Algebraic fractions have letters, or combinations of letters and numbers, in their numerator and their denominator.

To simplify algebraic fractions

1 Factorise.

2 Divide top and bottom by the HCF (or cancel common factors).

To multiply and divide algebraic fractions you use the same rules as for multiplying and dividing numerical fractions. Always remember to look for any common factors.

When adding or subtracting algebraic fractions, the rules are the same as for numerical fractions. Before you find the LCM of the denominators, you must factorise if possible.

21.1 Further simultaneous equations

1 Use the method of substitution to solve each of the following pairs of simultaneous equations.

State clearly the points of intersection of the straight line and the quadratic curve in each case.

a $y = x + 7$
$\quad y = x^2 - 5$

b $y = x + 5$
$\quad y = x^2 + 5x$

c $y = 2x$
$\quad y = x^2 - 4x + 8$

d $y = 4x - 2$
$\quad y = x^2 + 2$

e $y = x - 2$
$\quad y = 2x^2 + 8x + 1$

f $y = 3x - 2$
$\quad y^2 = 6x - 5$

A*

2 Solve this pair of simultaneous equations.

$\quad y = 4x - 4$
$\quad y = x^2 + 2x - 3$

Explain the geometrical significance of your answer.

21.2 Algebraic fractions

1 Simplify the following.

a $\dfrac{5x + 15}{10}$

b $\dfrac{8x}{8 - 2x}$

c $\dfrac{12x^2}{18x^2y^2}$

d $\dfrac{xy - 3x}{xy}$

e $\dfrac{5x + 10}{7x + 14}$

f $\dfrac{x - 4}{(x - 4)^2}$

B

2 Work these out, simplifying your answers where possible.

a $\dfrac{x}{5} \times \dfrac{x}{4}$

b $\dfrac{x}{8} \div \dfrac{y}{4}$

c $\dfrac{4x}{5} \times \dfrac{x + 5}{2}$

3 Work these out, simplifying your answers.

a $\dfrac{5a}{3} + \dfrac{3a}{5}$

b $\dfrac{1}{a} - \dfrac{2}{b}$

c $\dfrac{2a + 1}{3} + \dfrac{a - 4}{4}$

4 Solve the following.

a $\dfrac{x + 2}{5} + \dfrac{x + 1}{2} = 3$

b $\dfrac{3x + 1}{10} - \dfrac{5x - 1}{14} = 0$

c $\dfrac{2x - 3}{3} - \dfrac{4x - 5}{4} = 1$

5 One third of a number added to one tenth of the number is equal to seventeen less than the number.

   a Write expressions for 'one third of a number', 'one tenth of the number' and 'seventeen less than the number'.

   b Use these expressions to write an equation.

   c Solve the equation to find the original number.

6 On a school sports day, one fifth of all the students were competing, half were watching and one eighth were on a geography field trip. The remaining 140 students stayed at home.

   a Using x to represent the total number of students in the school, write expressions for the number of students competing, watching and on the field trip.

   b Write an equation in x.

   c Solve the equation to find the total number of students in the school.

7 A quarter of a number added to a fifth of the number is equal to the number divided by 20, plus 2.

What is the number?

8 Simplify the following.

   a $\dfrac{x^2 + x - 6}{x^2 - 4x + 4}$ **b** $\dfrac{x^2 + 6x + 5}{x^2 - x - 2}$ **c** $\dfrac{x^2 - 4}{x^2 + 7x + 10}$

9 Work these out, simplifying your answers.

   a $\dfrac{8x^2}{5y^2} \times \dfrac{4x}{2y^2}$ **b** $\dfrac{2x^2 + 6x}{x^2 + 3x} \times \dfrac{x + 3}{2x}$ **c** $\dfrac{3x + 4}{20} \div \dfrac{6x + 8}{5}$

10 Work these out, simplifying your answers.

   a $\dfrac{x^2 - 16}{5} \times \dfrac{20}{x^2 + 8x + 16}$ **b** $\dfrac{x^2 + x - 6}{x^2 - 9} \div \dfrac{x^2 - 4}{x^2 - 3x}$ **c** $\dfrac{x^2 - 100}{x^2 - x} \div \dfrac{3x - 30}{3x^2 + 2x}$

11 Work these out, simplifying your answers.

   a $\dfrac{4}{a + 3} + \dfrac{4}{a + 2}$ **b** $\dfrac{4}{a + 3} + \dfrac{4}{a - 3}$ **c** $\dfrac{3}{a - 4} - \dfrac{4}{a - 3}$

12 Solve the following.

   a $\dfrac{6}{2x - 1} - \dfrac{8}{3x - 1} = 2$ **b** $\dfrac{12}{x} + \dfrac{12}{x + 1} = 7$ **c** $\dfrac{2}{x - 3} - \dfrac{6}{x + 2} = 1$

21.3 Changing the subject of more complicated formulae

1 Make x the subject of each of the following formulae.

   a $px - y = q - px$ **b** $px + y = p - qx$ **c** $a(x + p) = b(x + q)$

2 Make y the subject of each of the following formulae.

   a $\dfrac{3 - y}{3 + y} = x$ **b** $\dfrac{y + 3}{y + 4} = \dfrac{a}{b}$ **c** $\sqrt{\dfrac{5y}{y + 5}} = ab$

   d $2\pi\sqrt{\dfrac{y}{x}} = a$ **e** $xy^2 + 2\pi r = v - zy^2$ **f** $a(3y^2 + b) = c(t - 2y^2)$

3 The thickness, h (cm), of a puddle of liquid on a flat surface is given by

$$h = 2\sqrt{\dfrac{s}{gd}}$$

where s = surface tension (newtons per metre)

         g = acceleration due to gravity (m/s²)

         d = density of liquid (g/cm³)

   a Rearrange the formula to make d the subject.

   b Find the density of a liquid when $h = 0.36$ cm, $s = 487$ newtons per metre and $g = 9.8$ m/s².

Links to:
Higher Student Book
Ch22, pp.332–335

This section revises the number skills that you will need to use in Unit 3.

1 All of these fractions are equivalent to each other, except one.
Which one of these fractions is not equivalent to the others?

$\frac{9}{24}$ $\frac{15}{40}$ $\frac{6}{16}$ $\frac{18}{48}$ $\frac{21}{64}$ $\frac{12}{32}$

2 Write each of these percentages as a fraction in its lowest terms.

a 20%   b 36%   c $45\frac{1}{2}$%

3 Which is smaller, $\frac{2}{5}$ or 25%? Give a reason for your answer.

4 At a cricket match, there are 175 home supporters and 70 away supporters.

a Write the ratio of home supporters to away supporters in its simplest form.

b Write the ratio of home supporters to total supporters in its simplest form.

5 Work out the missing number in each of these calculations.

a $6 \times 7 - 25 = \square$ b $32 - 8 \times 3 = \square$ c $(32 + 28) \div 4 = \square$

d $25 + 4 \times \square = 51$ e $18 \times 3 - \square = -11$ f $(\square - 8) \times 3 = 6$

g $4 - 5^2 = \square$ h $9^2 - \square = 37$ i $8^2 \times \square = -32$

6 Simplify the ratio 15 hours : 5 days.

7 Complete these statements.

a The reciprocal of 10 is _____   b The reciprocal of $\frac{1}{3}$ is _____

c The reciprocal of $\frac{2}{5}$ is _____   d The reciprocal of $2\frac{1}{4}$ is _____

e The reciprocal of 0.8 is _____   f The reciprocal of 6.5 is _____

8 Round 37.6952 to

a one decimal place   b two decimal places   c three decimal places.

9 Round 4576 to

a one significant figure   b two significant figures   c three significant figures.

10 Round 0.068 217 to

a one significant figure   b two significant figures   c three significant figures.

11 Round the number in each of these statements to an appropriate degree of accuracy.

a The bank made a profit of £26 887 459.

b There were 46 523 spectators at the football match.

c The kitchen is 5.6425 m long.

d The distance between two cities is 358.449 km.

12 Calculate the following, giving your answers correct to three significant figures.

a 4.25^3 b 14.87^2 c $\sqrt{158}$ d $\sqrt[3]{0.502}$

Key Points

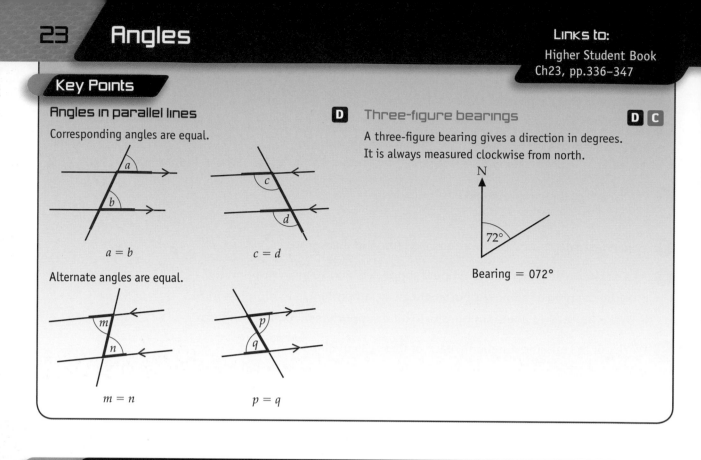

Angles in parallel lines **D**

Corresponding angles are equal.

$a = b$ $c = d$

Alternate angles are equal.

$m = n$ $p = q$

Three-figure bearings **D C**

A three-figure bearing gives a direction in degrees.
It is always measured clockwise from north.

N

72°

Bearing = 072°

23.1 Angles in parallel lines

D

1 Work out the sizes of the angles marked with letters. Give a reason for your answer each time.

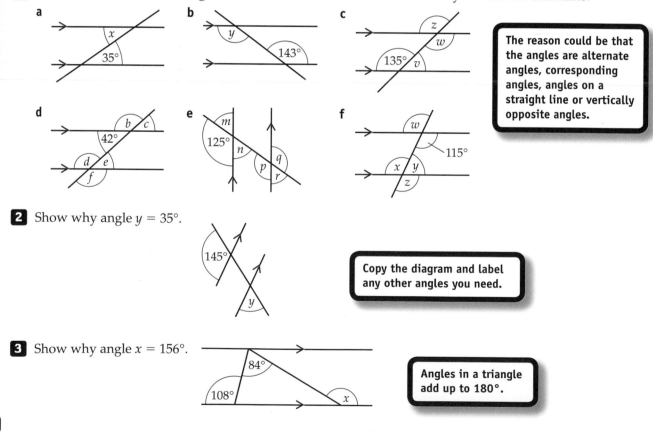

a
x
35°

b
y
143°

c
z
w
135° v

> The reason could be that the angles are alternate angles, corresponding angles, angles on a straight line or vertically opposite angles.

d
b c
42°
d e
f

e
m
125°
n
p q
r

f
w
115°
x y
z

D

2 Show why angle $y = 35°$.

145°
y

> Copy the diagram and label any other angles you need.

3 Show why angle $x = 156°$.

84°
108°
x

> Angles in a triangle add up to 180°.

4 Sam draws an isosceles trapezium. The top and bottom sides are parallel, and the other two sides are the same length.

She colours one of the base angles green and one of the top angles yellow.

She draws a diagonal, which bisects the green angle. The green angle is 70°.

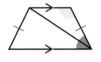

a Work out the size of the yellow angle.

Sam has another trapezium. It is not an isosceles trapezium.

The purple angle is 37° and the yellow angle is 118°.

b Work out the size of the red and blue angles.

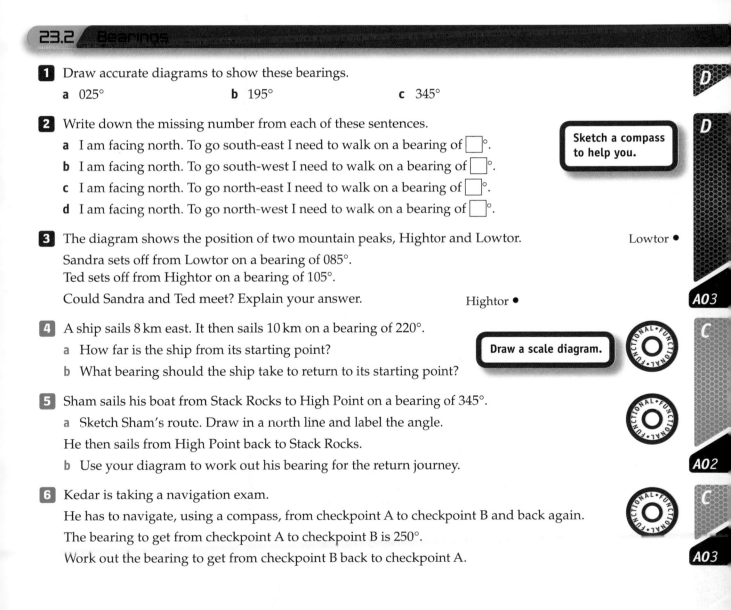

---

1 Draw accurate diagrams to show these bearings.

  a 025°   **b** 195°   **c** 345°

2 Write down the missing number from each of these sentences.

  a I am facing north. To go south-east I need to walk on a bearing of ☐°.

  b I am facing north. To go south-west I need to walk on a bearing of ☐°.

  c I am facing north. To go north-east I need to walk on a bearing of ☐°.

  d I am facing north. To go north-west I need to walk on a bearing of ☐°.

> Sketch a compass to help you.

3 The diagram shows the position of two mountain peaks, Hightor and Lowtor.

Sandra sets off from Lowtor on a bearing of 085°.

Ted sets off from Hightor on a bearing of 105°.

Could Sandra and Ted meet? Explain your answer.

Lowtor •

Hightor •

4 A ship sails 8 km east. It then sails 10 km on a bearing of 220°.

  a How far is the ship from its starting point?

  b What bearing should the ship take to return to its starting point?

> Draw a scale diagram.

5 Sham sails his boat from Stack Rocks to High Point on a bearing of 345°.

  a Sketch Sham's route. Draw in a north line and label the angle.

He then sails from High Point back to Stack Rocks.

  b Use your diagram to work out his bearing for the return journey.

6 Kedar is taking a navigation exam.

He has to navigate, using a compass, from checkpoint A to checkpoint B and back again.

The bearing to get from checkpoint A to checkpoint B is 250°.

Work out the bearing to get from checkpoint B back to checkpoint A.

Key Points

Triangle properties   **D**

The sum of the interior angles of a triangle is 180°.

The exterior angle of a triangle is equal to the sum of the two opposite interior angles.

Constructing triangles   **D**

To accurately construct a triangle given SAS (side angle side) or ASA (angle side angle) use a ruler and a protractor.

Leave in all of the construction lines.

Quadrilateral and polygon properties   **D** **C**

A quadrilateral is a 2-D shape bounded by four straight lines.

The angle sum of a quadrilateral is 360°.

The sum of the exterior angles of any polygon is 360°.

$$\text{exterior angle of a regular polygon} = \frac{360°}{\text{number of sides}}$$

the sum of the interior angles of any polygon is (number of sides − 2) × 180°.

interior angle = 180° − exterior angle

Drawing regular polygons by equal division of a circle   **D**

First calculate the angle at the centre of the polygon using 360° ÷ number of sides.

Then draw a circle, make a mark on the circumference and measure round one centre angle.

Use compasses to make the other marks on the circumference, and then join the marks with straight lines.

24.1   Triangle properties

D

1 Work out the value of x in each diagram.

a
5x, x, 3x

b
4x, 2x

c
2x, 3x

d
2x, 3x, 35°

e
62°, 5x, 83°

2 The diagram shows the plan view of part of a wooden seat.

The planks of wood used for each seat must be cut accurately so that the seats fit together with no gaps.

Angle x must be calculated before the plank is cut.

Calculate the size of angle x.

x, 72°

A02

24.2   Constructing triangles

D

1 a Draw an accurate copy of each of these triangles.

i
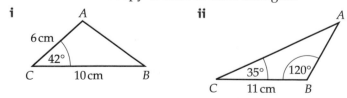
A, 6 cm, 42°, C, 10 cm, B

ii
A, 35°, 120°, C, 11 cm, B

b Write down the length AB for each of the triangles drawn in part **a**.

c Write down the size of $\angle BAC$ in each of the triangles drawn in part **a**.

2 **a** Draw an accurate copy of this triangle.

b Measure and write down the size of ∠XYZ.

c Measure and write down the length YZ.

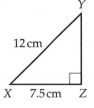

D

3 **a** Draw △PQR, where QR = 6 cm, ∠PQR = 105° and ∠PRQ = 52°.

b What is the length of the side PR?

> Sketch the triangle first.

AO2

4 A designer is finishing a plan of a children's slide. This is the sketch she has made.

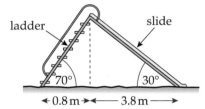

> Draw a scale drawing of the slide.

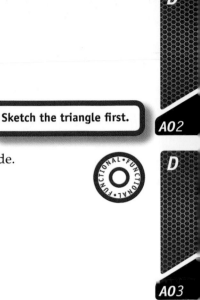

The designer says that the length of the ladder is about 2.3 m. Is she correct?

AO3

24.3 Quadrilaterals

1 A quadrilateral has interior angles of x, $2x$, 70° and 125°.

a Form an equation in x.

b Solve the equation to find the value of x.

D

2 For each quadrilateral

  i form an equation in x.

  ii solve the equation to find the value of x.

a

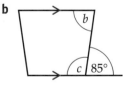

b

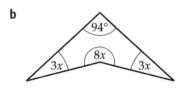

3 Work out the sizes of the angles marked with letters.

a

b

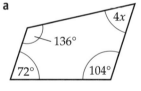

c

4 Work out the sizes of the angles marked with letters.

a

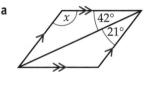

b

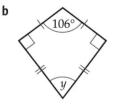

c

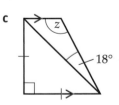

D

5 Marian works out angle x like this.

$x = 180 - 76 = 104°$

Alex works out angle x like this.

$x = \dfrac{360 - 76}{2} = 142°$

Is either of them correct? Show working to support your answer.

AO2

6 Work out the value of $3y - 6x$.

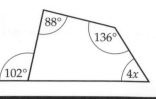

24.4 Polygons

D

1 Work out the size of angle x in each of these diagrams.

a

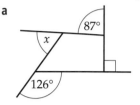

b

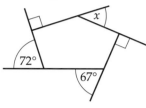

D

2 Work out the value of x in each of these polygons.

a

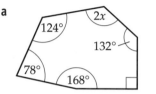

b

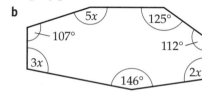

A02

D

3 The exterior angles of this polygon are w, x, y and z.

∠w is 30° more than ∠x.

∠y is 10° less than ∠x.

∠z is twice the size of ∠x.

A02   What is the size of ∠x?

C

4 Work out the size of the exterior angle of a regular polygon with 9 sides.

5 Work out the size of the interior angle of a regular polygon with 18 sides.

6 How many sides does a regular polygon have if the interior angle is 170°?

C

7 Explain why it is not possible for the exterior angle of a regular polygon to be 42°.

A02

C

8 A carpenter is making a wooden seat to go against a wall and around a pond. The seat is in the shape of half of a regular hexagon. The diagram shows a plan view of the seat.

At what angle, marked as x on the diagram, must the carpenter cut the wood for the seat?

A03

24.5 Drawing polygons

D

1 a Draw a circle of radius 5 cm.

b By equal division of a circle, draw a regular pentagon.

2 a Draw a circle of radius 8 cm.

b By equal division of a circle, draw a regular decagon.

> A decagon has 10 sides.

D

3 Is the length of the side of a regular hexagon drawn inside a 7 cm circle shorter or longer than the length of the side of an regular octagon drawn inside an 8.5 cm circle? Show working to support your answer.

A02

Key Points

Equations and formulae D C B A

You can solve problems by writing and solving equations.

You can use letters or words to write your own formulae.
You can substitute values into a formula and solve the equation to find the value of an unknown.

You can use the rules of algebra to rearrange a formula to make a different letter the subject.

Trial and improvement C

Some equations cannot be solved using algebra. Instead, you can solve them by trial and improvement.
Solve an equation by substituting values of x into the equation to see if they give the correct solution. The more values you try, the closer you can get to the solution.

25.1 Equations and formulae

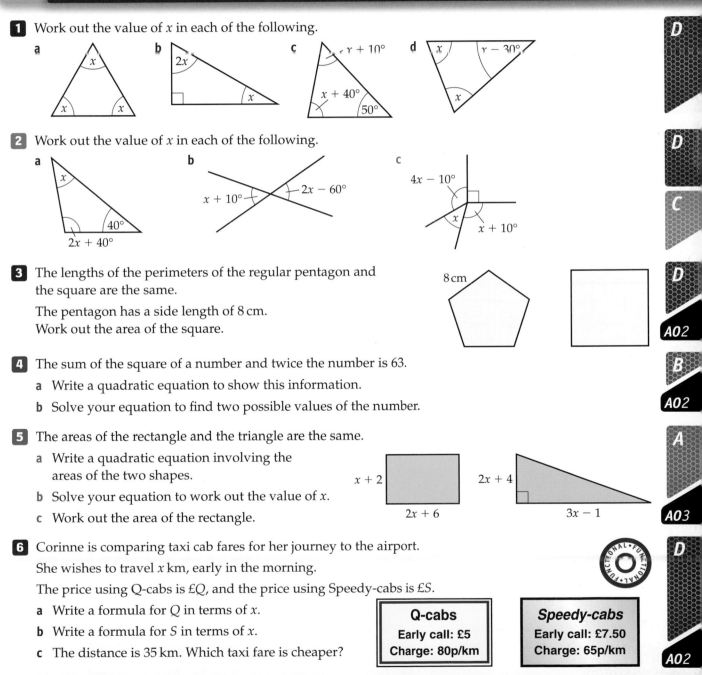

1 Work out the value of x in each of the following.

a

b $2x$

c $x + 10°$ $x + 40°$ $50°$

d x $x - 30°$ x

2 Work out the value of x in each of the following.

a x $40°$ $2x + 40°$

b $x + 10°$ $2x - 60°$

c $4x - 10°$ x $x + 10°$

3 The lengths of the perimeters of the regular pentagon and the square are the same.

The pentagon has a side length of 8 cm.
Work out the area of the square.

8 cm

4 The sum of the square of a number and twice the number is 63.

a Write a quadratic equation to show this information.

b Solve your equation to find two possible values of the number.

5 The areas of the rectangle and the triangle are the same.

a Write a quadratic equation involving the areas of the two shapes.

b Solve your equation to work out the value of x.

c Work out the area of the rectangle.

$x + 2$ $2x + 6$ $2x + 4$ $3x - 1$

6 Corinne is comparing taxi cab fares for her journey to the airport.

She wishes to travel x km, early in the morning.

The price using Q-cabs is £Q, and the price using Speedy-cabs is £S.

a Write a formula for Q in terms of x.

b Write a formula for S in terms of x.

c The distance is 35 km. Which taxi fare is cheaper?

Q-cabs
Early call: £5
Charge: 80p/km

Speedy-cabs
Early call: £7.50
Charge: 65p/km

D
D
C
D
AO2
B
AO2
A
AO3
D
AO2

7 The length of a rectangle is 5 cm more than its width, w.

    a Write a formula for the area of the rectangle, A.

    b Work out the value of w, when $A = 126 \text{ cm}^2$.

8 The formula for the volume of a pyramid is $V = \frac{1}{3} \times$ base area $\times$ height.

    a Rearrange the formula to make 'base area' the subject.

    b Use your rearranged formula to work out the base area of this square-based pyramid.

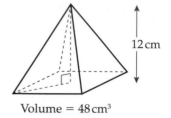

12 cm

Volume = 48 cm³

25.2   Trial and improvement

1 Jimmy is using trial and improvement to solve the equation $x^3 + 4x = 90$.

His first three trials are shown in the table.

x	$x^3 + 4x$	Comment
3	39	too low
4	80	too low
5	145	too high

Complete the table to find a solution to the equation.

Give your answer correct to one decimal place.

2 Mia is using trial and improvement to solve the equation $x\sqrt{x} = 50$.

Her first two trials are shown in the table.

x	$x\sqrt{x}$	Comment
15	58.09	too high
13	46.87	too low

Complete the table to find a solution to the equation.

Give your answer correct to one decimal place.

3 The area of this rectangle is 400 cm^2.

    a Write an equation showing this information.

    b Use trial and improvement to find the value of x correct to one decimal place.

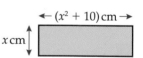

$\leftarrow (x^2 + 10)\text{ cm} \rightarrow$

x cm

4 Use the formula $R = \dfrac{y^2 + 3y^3}{4}$ to find the value of y when $R = 38$.

Use trial and improvement and give your answer correct to one decimal place.

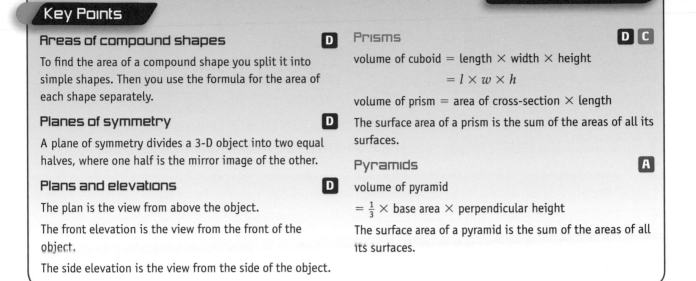

Key Points

Areas of compound shapes D

To find the area of a compound shape you split it into simple shapes. Then you use the formula for the area of each shape separately.

Planes of symmetry D

A plane of symmetry divides a 3-D object into two equal halves, where one half is the mirror image of the other.

Plans and elevations D

The plan is the view from above the object.

The front elevation is the view from the front of the object.

The side elevation is the view from the side of the object.

Prisms D C

volume of cuboid = length × width × height
$$= l \times w \times h$$

volume of prism = area of cross-section × length

The surface area of a prism is the sum of the areas of all its surfaces.

Pyramids A

volume of pyramid
$$= \tfrac{1}{3} \times \text{base area} \times \text{perpendicular height}$$

The surface area of a pyramid is the sum of the areas of all its surfaces.

26.1 Perimeter and area of compound shapes

1 Calculate the perimeter and area of each of these compound shapes. **D**

a

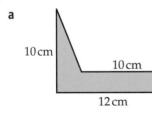

$12 + 8 + $

b

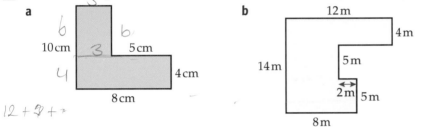

2 Calculate the areas of these shapes.

a

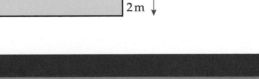

b

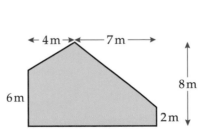

26.2 Planes of symmetry

1 Copy these 3-D objects on squared paper. **D**

For each object, show all its planes of symmetry.

Draw a separate diagram for each plane of symmetry.

a

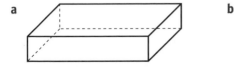

b

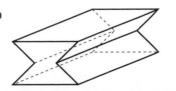

D **1** For each block of cubes, draw

    i a plan view   **ii** a front elevation   **iii** a side elevation from the right-hand side.

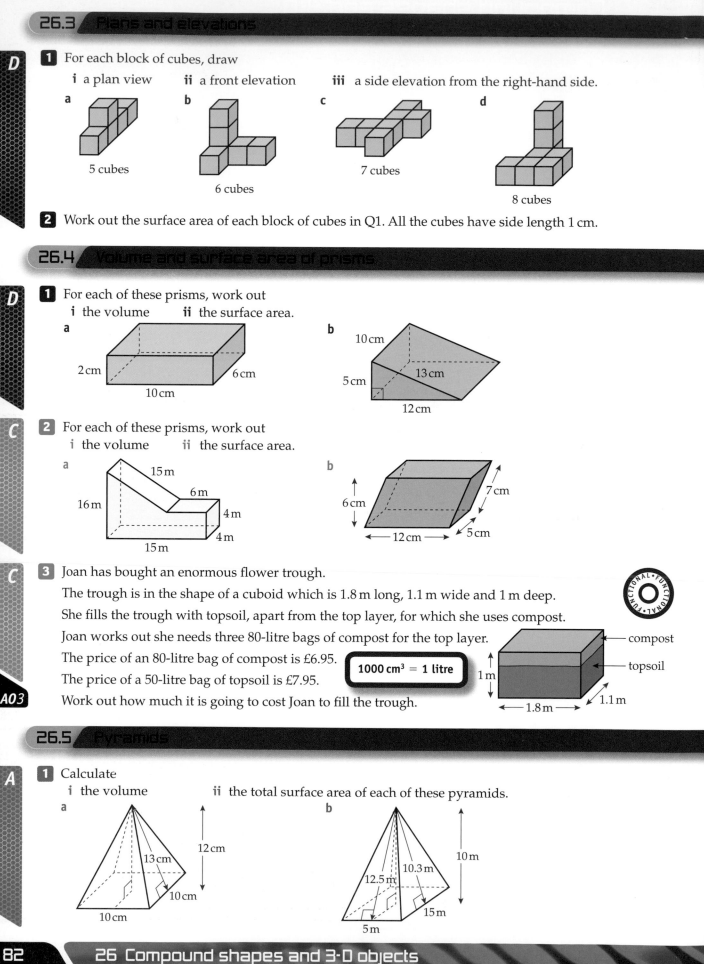

a

5 cubes

b

6 cubes

c

7 cubes

d

8 cubes

    2 Work out the surface area of each block of cubes in Q1. All the cubes have side length 1 cm.

26.4 Volume and surface area of prisms

D **1** For each of these prisms, work out

    i the volume   **ii** the surface area.

a

2 cm 6 cm 10 cm

b

10 cm 13 cm 5 cm 12 cm

C **2** For each of these prisms, work out

    i the volume   **ii** the surface area.

a

15 m 6 m 16 m 4 m 4 m 15 m

b

6 cm 7 cm 12 cm 5 cm

C **3** Joan has bought an enormous flower trough.

The trough is in the shape of a cuboid which is 1.8 m long, 1.1 m wide and 1 m deep.

She fills the trough with topsoil, apart from the top layer, for which she uses compost.

Joan works out she needs three 80-litre bags of compost for the top layer.

The price of an 80-litre bag of compost is £6.95.

The price of a 50-litre bag of topsoil is £7.95.

| 1000 cm³ = 1 litre |

compost
topsoil
1 m
1.8 m
1.1 m

AO3 Work out how much it is going to cost Joan to fill the trough.

26.5 Pyramids

A **1** Calculate

    i the volume   **ii** the total surface area of each of these pyramids.

a

12 cm 13 cm 10 cm 10 cm

b

10 m 12.5 m 10.3 m 15 m 5 m

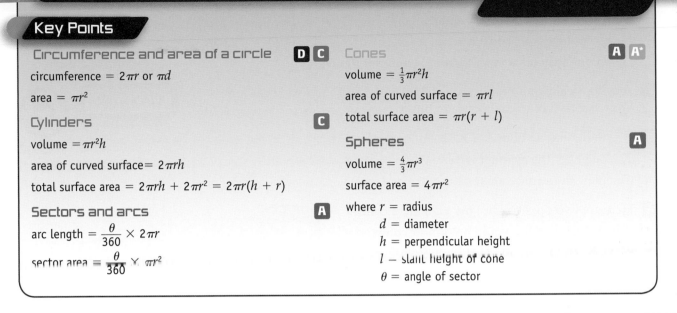

Key Points

Circumference and area of a circle **D** **C**

circumference $= 2\pi r$ or πd

area $= \pi r^2$

Cylinders

volume $= \pi r^2 h$

area of curved surface $= 2\pi rh$

total surface area $= 2\pi rh + 2\pi r^2 = 2\pi r(h + r)$

Sectors and arcs **A**

arc length $= \dfrac{\theta}{360} \times 2\pi r$

sector area $= \dfrac{\theta}{360} \times \pi r^2$

Cones **A** **A⁺**

volume $= \frac{1}{3}\pi r^2 h$

area of curved surface $= \pi rl$

total surface area $= \pi r(r + l)$ **C**

Spheres **A**

volume $= \frac{4}{3}\pi r^3$

surface area $= 4\pi r^2$

where r = radius
d = diameter
h = perpendicular height
l = slant height of cone
θ = angle of sector

27.1 Area and circumference of a circle

1 Calculate the diameter of a circle with a circumference of 12 m.
Give your answer to two decimal places. **D**

2 Work out the radius of a circle with an area of $36\pi\,\text{cm}^2$.

3 A car tyre with a diameter of 70 cm travels 15 000 km. **D**
How many revolutions, to the nearest 100, has the tyre completed?

AO3

4 Calculate the perimeter of this semicircle. **C**
Give your answer to two decimal places.

←—— 16 cm ——→

5 A circular pond has a line of bricks around the circumference. **C**
The radius of the pond is 0.8 m.
What length of bricks is needed?
Give your answer to the nearest centimetre.

←0.8 m→

AO2

6 This diagram shows the inside
line of a running track. **C**
 a The area inside the running track is grass.
   What is the area of the grass?
 b There are eight lanes. Each lane is 1.25 m wide.
   What is the total length of the outside lane's outer line?
   Give your answer to the nearest metre.

73 m

←—— 85 m ——→

7 Calculate the shaded area of this shape.
Give your answer to two decimal places.

2 cm

←——————— 12 cm ———————→

AO3

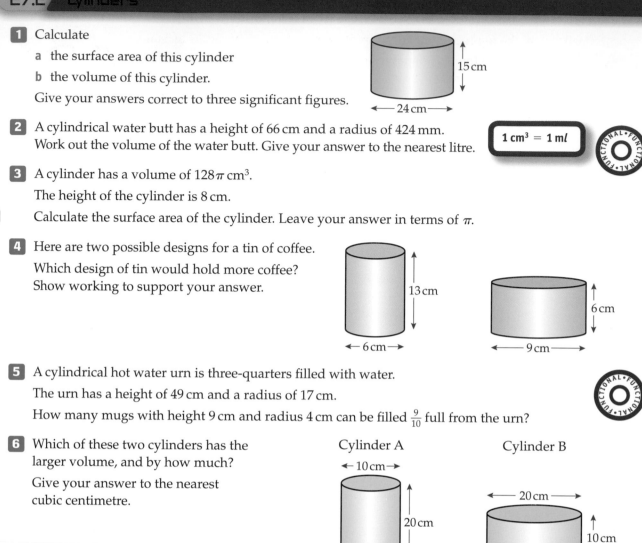

C **1** Calculate

    a the surface area of this cylinder

    b the volume of this cylinder.

    Give your answers correct to three significant figures.

15 cm

24 cm

2 A cylindrical water butt has a height of 66 cm and a radius of 424 mm.
Work out the volume of the water butt. Give your answer to the nearest litre.

$1\,\text{cm}^3 = 1\,\text{m}l$

C
AO3 **3** A cylinder has a volume of $128\pi\,\text{cm}^3$.

    The height of the cylinder is 8 cm.

    Calculate the surface area of the cylinder. Leave your answer in terms of π.

C **4** Here are two possible designs for a tin of coffee.

    Which design of tin would hold more coffee?
Show working to support your answer.

13 cm

6 cm

6 cm

9 cm

5 A cylindrical hot water urn is three-quarters filled with water.

    The urn has a height of 49 cm and a radius of 17 cm.

    How many mugs with height 9 cm and radius 4 cm can be filled $\frac{9}{10}$ full from the urn?

6 Which of these two cylinders has the
larger volume, and by how much?

    Give your answer to the nearest
cubic centimetre.

Cylinder A

Cylinder B

10 cm

20 cm

20 cm

10 cm

AO2

A **1** This diagram shows a sector of a circle.

    Work out

    a the arc length

    b the area.

    Give your answers correct to two decimal places.

5 cm

305°

A **2** A box of chocolates is in the shape of a sector of a circle.

    There is a ribbon around the perimeter of the box.

    There is a 10 mm overlap of ribbon.

    What is the length of ribbon needed to go around the box?
Give your answer to the nearest millimetre.

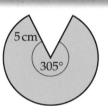

20 cm 120°

3 Which has the larger area?

    A The sector of a circle with radius 6.5 cm and an angle at the centre of 75°.

AO2   **B** The sector of a circle with radius 5.1 cm and an angle at the centre of 123°.

4 Hannah designs and makes pendants. This is one of her designs.

The large ring has an outer radius of 40 mm and an inner radius of 37 mm.

The small ring at the top has an outer radius of 8 mm and an inner radius of 5 mm.

Inside the large ring are four overlapping sectors of circles.
Each sector has an angle at the centre of 130°.

The largest sector has an outer radius of 4 cm and
an inner radius of 1.5 cm.

The other sectors have
- outer radius 3 cm, inner radius 1 cm
- outer radius 2 cm, inner radius 0.5 cm
- outer radius 1 cm.

Work out the total visible area of this design.

Give your answer correct to three significant figures.

A

A03

27.4 Cones

1 Calculate

a the surface area of this cone

b the volume of this cone.

Give your answers correct to
the nearest whole number.

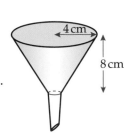

15 cm   15.8 cm   5 cm

A

2 A funnel for pouring oil is made from plastic.

The funnel is a cone with a tube at the bottom.

Calculate the volume that the cone section of the funnel can hold.
Give your answer to the nearest m*l*.

4 cm   8 cm

3 A gold pendant in the shape of a cone is melted down to make a cylindrical pendant.

The cone pendant has a height of 12 mm and radius 5 mm.

The cylindrical pendant has a height of 8 mm.

What is the radius of the cylindrical pendant? Give your answer to one decimal place.

A

A03

4 The cone in the diagram has its top 3 cm cut off as shown.

a Calculate the volume of the original cone.

b Calculate the volume of the cone that is cut off.

c Calculate the volume of the frustum.

Leave your answers in terms of π.

3 cm   9 cm   2 cm   6 cm

A*

A03

A02

5 Calculate the volume of this frustum of a cone.
Give your answer correct to three significant figures.

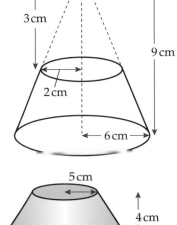

5 cm   4 cm   10 cm

A*

A03

A

1 Calculate
   a the surface area of this sphere
   b the volume of this sphere.
   Give your answers correct to three significant figures.

5.2 cm

2 Calculate the volume and surface area of a sphere with diameter of 84 mm.
Give your answers to the nearest cubic and square millimetre respectively.

3 A sphere has a volume of $972\pi\,\text{cm}^3$.
Work out
   a the radius of the sphere
   b the surface area of the sphere.
   Leave your answer to part **b** in terms of π.

A

4 A sphere has a surface area of $100\pi\,\text{cm}^2$.
Work out the volume of the sphere.
Leave your answer in terms of π.

5 A glass ball has a radius of 25 mm and a mass of 157 g.
Work out the density, in g/cm^3, of the glass.
Give your answer correct to one decimal place.

A02

A

6 Eight spheres of radius 5 cm fit exactly inside a cubical box.
Calculate the volume of empty space in the box.
Give your answer to the nearest cm^3.

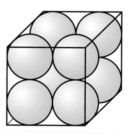

7 A hemispherical glass paperweight of radius 5 cm is packed into a box.
The box has dimensions 10.5 cm by 10.5 cm by 5.5 cm.
Once the paperweight is in, the empty space in the box is filled with packing.
What volume of packing is needed to fill the box?
Give your answer to the nearest cm^3.

A hemisphere is
half a sphere.

A03

Links to:
Higher Student Book
Ch28, pp.410–421

Key Points

Converting areas and volumes D C

You can convert units of area using

- $1 \text{ cm}^2 = 100 \text{ mm}^2$
- $1 \text{ m}^2 = 10\,000 \text{ cm}^2$
- $1 \text{ km}^2 = 1\,000\,000 \text{ m}^2$

You can convert units of volume using

- $1 \text{ cm}^3 = 1000 \text{ mm}^3$
- $1 \text{ m}^2 = 1\,000\,000 \text{ cm}^3$
- $1 \text{ litre} = 1000 \text{ cm}^3$

Speed D C

Speed is a measurement of how fast something is travelling.

$$\text{speed} = \frac{\text{distance}}{\text{time}}$$

$$\text{distance} = \text{speed} \times \text{time}$$

$$\text{time} = \frac{\text{distance}}{\text{speed}}$$

Density C B

Density is a measurement of the amount of a substance contained in a certain volume.

$$\text{density} = \frac{\text{mass}}{\text{volume}}$$

$$\text{mass} = \text{density} \times \text{volume}$$

$$\text{volume} = \frac{\text{mass}}{\text{density}}$$

Dimension theory B

- Length is a one-dimensional quantity.

In a formula for length, each term must contain one letter representing length.

- Area is a two-dimensional quantity.

In a formula for area, each term must contain either two lengths multiplied together or one letter representing area.

- Volume is a three-dimensional quantity.

In a formula for volume, each term must contain either three lengths multiplied together, a length multiplied by an area or one letter representing volume.

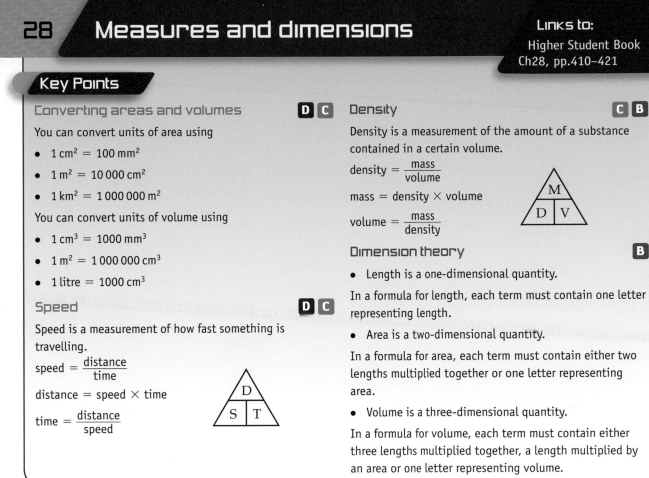

28.1 Converting areas and volumes

1 Copy and complete these conversions.   **D**

a $3 \text{ m}^2 = \boxed{300}\text{cm}^2$

b $7.6 \text{ m}^2 = \boxed{7}\,\text{cm}^2$

c $0.5 \text{ m}^2 = \boxed{}\text{cm}^2$

d $1800 \text{ cm}^2 = \boxed{}\text{m}^2$

e $8 \text{ km}^2 = \boxed{}\text{m}^2$

f $33\,000 \text{ m}^2 = \boxed{}\text{km}^2$

g $1000 \text{ mm}^2 = \boxed{}\text{cm}^2$

> The answer to part a is not 300 cm².

2 Clive's garage is a rectangle 660 cm long and 250 cm wide.   **D**

He is going to paint the floor with a non-slip covering.

The price of a 1 litre pot is £6.25 and it will cover 2.5 m².

The price of a $2\frac{1}{2}$ litre pot is £14.50 and it will cover 6.25 m².

What is the cheapest way for Clive to paint the floor, and how much will it cost him?   **A03**

3 Copy and complete these conversions.   **C**

a $5\,550\,000 \text{ cm}^3 = \boxed{}\text{m}^3$

b $3750 \text{ cm}^3 = \boxed{}\text{litres}$

c $0.6 \text{ m}^3 = \boxed{}\text{cm}^3$

d $1.86 \text{ m}^3 = \boxed{}\text{litres}$

e $2.7 \text{ cm}^3 = \boxed{}\text{mm}^3$

f $2.7 \text{ cm}^3 = \boxed{}\text{m}l$

4 Adam's power hose puts 1250 cm^3 of water per second into a swimming pool. The swimming pool is in the shape of a cuboid with dimensions 25 m by 12 m by 1.5 m.   **C**

How many hours will it take Adam to fill his swimming pool?   **A03**

D

1 Work out the average speed for each of these journeys.

   a A snail moves 18 m in $1\frac{1}{2}$ hours.

     Write your answer in
      i m/hour   **ii** m/s

   b A baby crawls 18 m in 4 minutes.

     Write your answer in
      i m/minute   **ii** m/s

   c A woman runs 180 m in 24 seconds.

2 A Japanese 'bullet train' travels at 205 km/h for 15 minutes.

   How far does it travel during this time?

D

3 Many roads in Spain have a speed limit of 100 km/h.

   Write this speed limit in mph.

4 Convert

   a 75 km/h into m/s

   b 140 m/s into km/h.

5 Linda drives 85 km in 1 hour and 15 minutes, then stops for 10 minutes to get some petrol.

   She then drives for a further 125 km, which takes her 1 hour and 35 minutes.

AO2

   Work out her average speed for the whole journey.

C

6 Jamie jogs 5.7 km (correct to one decimal place) in 45 minutes (correct to the nearest minute).

   Find the upper and lower bounds for his average speed in km/h.

   Give your answers correct to two decimal places.

7 A car travels from London to Bristol at an average speed of 52 mph, correct to the nearest whole number. The journey is 100 miles, correct to the nearest 10 miles.

   Baz says that the journey will definitely take less than 2 hours.

   a Show working to explain why Baz is wrong.

AO3

   b Calculate the shortest possible time it could take.

C

1 Gold has a density of 19.3 g/cm³.

   a Find the mass of 3 cm³ of gold.   **b** Find the volume of 150 g of gold.

2 A cube of oak has volume 64 cm³. Its mass is 54.4 g.

   Calculate the density of the oak.

C

3 An aluminium cube of side length 5 cm has a mass of 337.5 g.

   a Work out the volume of the cube.

   b Calculate the density of aluminium.

AO2

   c Calculate the mass of an aluminium cube of side length 10 cm.

4 The fuel tank on a lorry holds 300 litres of diesel.

   a Convert 300 litres into cm^3.

Diesel has a density of $0.85\,g/cm^3$.

   b Calculate the total mass of diesel when the fuel tank is full.

     Give your answer in kg.

5 The diagram shows a cylindrical concrete pillar.

The concrete has a density of $7.5\,g/cm^3$.

A crane can lift a maximum mass of 2 tonnes.

Can the crane lift the pillar? Show working to support your answer.

2.4 m

0.4 m

6 The lightest type of balsa wood has a density of $0.04\,g/cm^3$ to one significant figure.

A block of this wood has a volume of $47\,000\,cm^3$ to two significant figures.

Calculate the greatest and the least possible values for the mass of the block.

7 This block of wood has a cross-sectional area of $0.010\,m^2$ and length of 1.5 m.

The block has a mass of 20 kg.

All measurements are accurate to two significant figures.

Calculate the greatest possible value for the density of the wood.

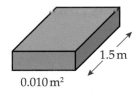

1.5 m

$0.010\,m^2$

28.4 Dimension theory

1 A and B are areas, and x, y and z are lengths.

Say whether each of these expressions represents a length, an area, a volume or none of these.

  a $A + B$ **b** xA **c** $3xyz$ **d** $\frac{4}{3}\pi y^3$

  e $A + yz$ **f** $2x(x + y)$ **g** $x(5xy^2 + y^3)$ **h** $x(5A)$

2 George writes down the following formula for the volume of a square-based pyramid.

$V = \frac{1}{3}bh$, where b and h are lengths.

Use dimensions to show why his formula must be wrong.

3 Which formula is most likely to be correct for the area of this shape?

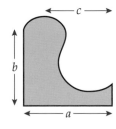

c

b

a

 A $A = \dfrac{ab - (34c^2 - 15b^2)}{a^2}$ **B** $A = \dfrac{4a(b^2 - c^2)}{3c}$ **C** $A = \dfrac{3ab - 2b^2 + bc}{a + b}$

4 A florist sells cylindrical vases in different sizes.

This notice is displayed by the vases.

Do you think the notice will provide an accurate guide for all the different sizes of vases?

Give a reason for your answer.

> Amount of flower food per vase $= \dfrac{R^4}{50}$ grams (R is the radius of the vase).

Key Points

Constructions

Constructions must be drawn using only a straight edge (ruler) and compasses.

Leave all construction lines and arcs on the diagram as evidence you have used the correct method.

Perpendicular at a point on a line

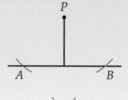

Perpendicular from a point to a line

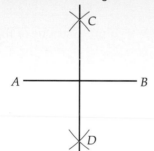

Perpendicular bisector of a line segment

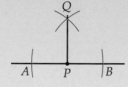

C Angle of 60°

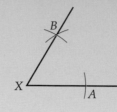

The bisector of an angle

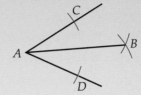

Locus **C** **B**

The locus of points that are the same distance from a fixed point is a circle.

The locus of points that are the same distance from a fixed line is two parallel lines, one each side of the given line.

The locus of points that are the same distance from a fixed line segment AB is a 'racetrack' shape. The shape has two lines parallel to AB and two semicircular ends.

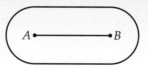

The locus of points equidistant from two fixed points is the perpendicular bisector of the line segment joining the two points.

The locus of points equidistant from two fixed lines is the angle bisector of the angle formed by the lines.

29.1 Constructions

C

1 a Draw an equilateral triangle with sides of length 8 cm.

b Construct the perpendicular bisector of each side of your triangle.

c Put your compasses on the point where your bisectors cross, open them out to one of the vertices of the triangle and draw a circle. What do you notice?

2 Construct the perpendicular from a point P to a line segment QR.

$P \bullet$

$Q \rule{3cm}{0.4pt} R$

3 **a** Draw a line segment QR, 12 cm long.

b Mark the point P on the line, 8 cm from Q.

c Construct the perpendicular at point P.

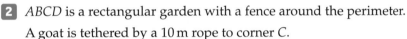

4 **a** Use a protractor to draw an angle of 80°.

b Using compasses to construct the bisector of the angle.

c Use a protractor to measure the two angles you created.

d How accurate was your construction?

5 Using only a ruler and compasses, make an accurate construction of this triangle. Leave in all of your construction lines.

29.2 Locus

1 Make a copy of this letter L.

Draw the locus of the points that are exactly 2 cm from the L.

2 $ABCD$ is a rectangular garden with a fence around the perimeter.

A goat is tethered by a 10 m rope to corner C.
There is a shed along the fence AC as shown.

a Draw a scale diagram of the garden using a scale of 1 cm = 2 m.

b Show on the diagram all the possible positions of the goat if the rope remains tight.

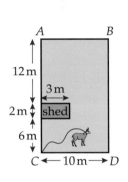

3 A horse is tethered to the corner of a rectangular field by a 12 m rope.
The field measures 15 m by 30 m.

Show by calculation that the horse can graze just over 25% of the field.

4 The diagram shows Mr Jones' garden. He wants to plant a tree nearer to the edge AB than to the edge AD.
He wants to plant the tree within 3 m of the seat S.

a Draw a scale diagram of the garden.

b Construct the locus of points that are the same distance from AB as they are from AD.

c Draw the locus of points that are exactly 3 m from S.

d Shade the region inside the garden where Mr Jones can plant his tree.

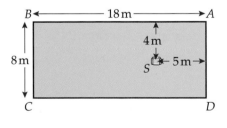

5 Make an accurate copy of triangle ABC.

Shade the region where the points are nearer to B than to A, and closer to BC than to AB.

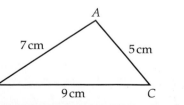

Key Points

Reflection D C

To describe a reflection on a grid you need to give the equation of the mirror line.

Translation D C

To describe a translation you have to give the distance and direction of movement.

You can describe a translation using a column vector, for example $\binom{3}{2}$ means move 3 in the x-direction and then move 2 in the y-direction.

Rotation D C

To describe a rotation fully, you need to give

• the centre of the rotation
• the size of turn
• the direction of turn.

Combined transformations C

Reflections, translations and rotations are transformations. They transform an object to an image. For these transformations, the object and its image are congruent.

You can combine transformations by doing one, then another.

30.1 Reflection on a coordinate grid

D

1 Copy this coordinate grid.

  a Draw the reflection of triangle A in the line $y = 3$.
  Label the reflected shape B.

  b Draw the reflection of triangle A in the line $x = -1$.
  Label the reflected shape C.

  c Triangle D is a reflection of triangle A in a mirror line.
  Describe this transformation.

AO2

C

2 Describe the transformation that takes

  a shape A to shape B

  b shape A to shape C.

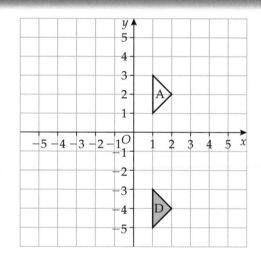

AO2

3 Alice starts with this shape.

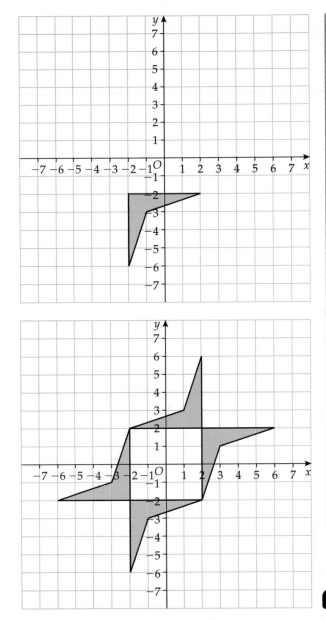

She transforms the shape to make this pattern.

Describe the transformations she uses.

30.2 Translation

1 Copy the following shapes on to squared paper.

Draw the image of the shape after the given translation.

a

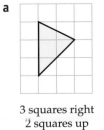

3 squares right
2 squares up

b

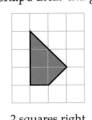

2 squares right
3 squares down

c

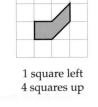

1 square left
4 squares up

2 On this grid, shape M is translated to shape N. Describe the translation.

C

3 Write down the column vector for each of the following translations.

a Triangle P to triangle Q.

b Triangle Q to triangle R.

c Triangle R to triangle P.

d Triangle P to triangle R.

e What do you notice about your answers in parts c and d?

4 On a grid, shape X is translated to shape Y by the vector $\begin{pmatrix} 4 \\ 7 \end{pmatrix}$ and shape Y is translated to shape Z by the vector $\begin{pmatrix} 2 \\ -8 \end{pmatrix}$.

A02

a Write down the column vector that translates shape X directly to shape Z.

b Write down the column vector that translates shape Z directly to shape X.

30.3

D

1 Copy each shape and the centre of rotation on to squared paper.

Draw the image of the shape after the rotation given.

a

b

$\frac{1}{4}$ turn clockwise about centre C $\frac{1}{2}$ turn anticlockwise about centre C

For Q2 to Q4, copy this coordinate grid and draw shapes L, M and N.

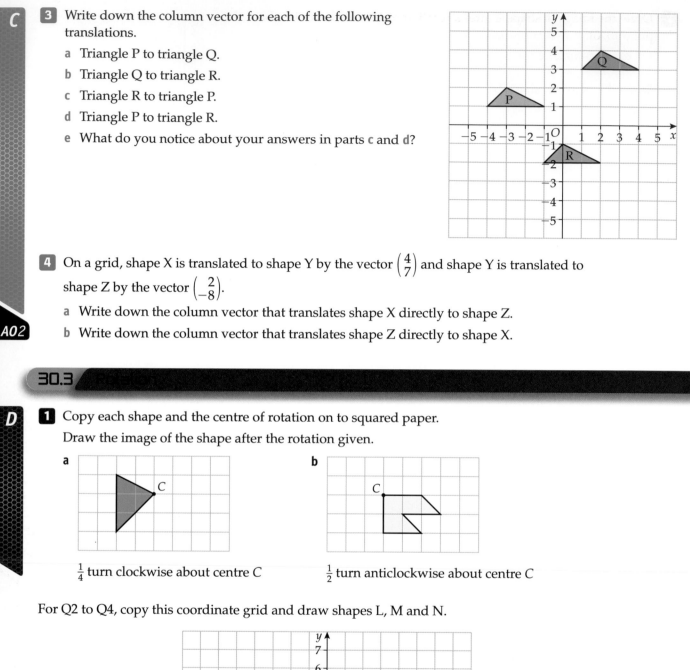

2 Draw the image of shape L after a rotation of 90° anticlockwise about the point (0, 0).
Label your image 2.

3 Draw the image of shape M after a rotation of 180° about the point (2, 1).
Label your image 3.

4 Rotate shape N about the point (2, −1) to make a pattern with rotational symmetry of order 4.

For Q5 and Q6 use this coordinate grid.

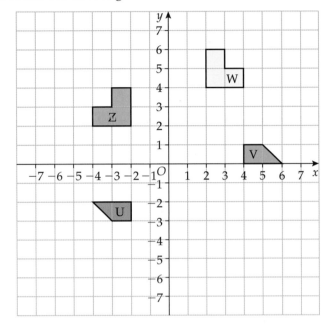

5 Shape U rotates on to shape V.

  a What size turn is the rotation?

  b Find the centre of rotation and write down the coordinates.

6 Describe fully the transformation that maps shape W on to shape Z.

7 A children's fairground wheel has six seats.

The seats are at the end of arms which are spaced equally around a centre hub.
Each seat and arm looks like this.

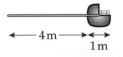

4 m   1 m

Make a simplified scale drawing of the wheel on a coordinate grid.

Use a scale of 1 grid division to 1 metre.

C

1 Copy this diagram.

a Translate shape U by column vector $\begin{pmatrix} -7 \\ 5 \end{pmatrix}$. Label the image V.

b Translate shape V by column vector $\begin{pmatrix} 3 \\ -9 \end{pmatrix}$. Label the image W.

c Write down the column vector for the transformation that takes shape U directly to shape W.

d Write down the column vector that takes shape W directly to shape U.

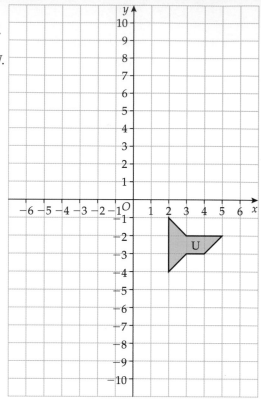

2 Copy shape R on to a coordinate grid.

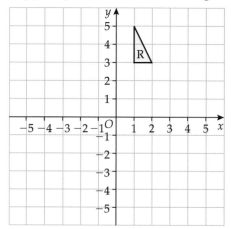

a Rotate shape R 90° clockwise about $(-1, 2)$. Label the image S.

b Rotate shape S 90° clockwise about $(-2, 0)$. Label the image T.

c Describe the single transformation that takes shape T back to shape R.

3 Copy shape E on to a coordinate grid.

a Reflect shape E in the line $y = 2$. Label the image F.

b Reflect shape F in the line $y = -x$. Label the image G.

c Describe the single transformation that takes shape G back to shape E.

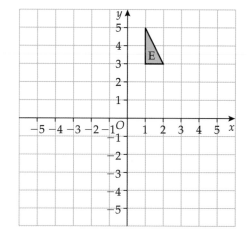

C

AO3

4 A reflection in the line $y = x$ is the equivalent of two transformations, T1 followed by T2. Give two possible descriptions of the transformations T1 and T2.

C

5 Copy shape L on to a coordinate grid.

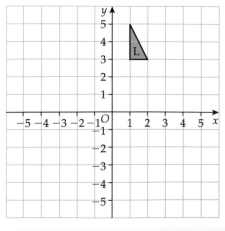

a Rotate shape L 90° anticlockwise about $(1, 0)$. Label the image M.

b Reflect shape M in the line $y = -1$. Label the image N.

c Translate shape N by column vector $\begin{pmatrix} -1 \\ 1 \end{pmatrix}$. Label the image P.

d Describe the single transformation that takes shape P back to shape L.

Key Points

Enlargement D C A

An enlargement changes the size of an object but not its shape. The number of times each length of a shape is enlarged is called the scale factor.

In an enlargement, all the angles stay the same but all the lengths change in the same proportion. The image is similar to the object.

A scale factor greater than 1 gives an image that is larger than the object.

A scale factor between 0 and 1 gives an image that is smaller than the object.

An enlargement with a negative scale factor produces an image that is the other side of the centre of enlargement. The image appears upside down, and its size is determined by the scale factor.

To describe an enlargement fully you must give the scale factor and the centre of enlargement.

31.1 Enlargement

1 The vertices of a rectangle are at (1, 1), (1, 3), (5, 3) and (5, 1).

a Enlarge the rectangle by a scale factor of 2, using (0, 0) as the centre of enlargement.

b What are the coordinates of the vertices of the image rectangle?

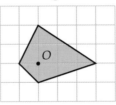

D

2 A shape has a perimeter of 18 cm. It is enlarged by a scale factor of 4.

What is the perimeter of the enlargement?

3 Copy each of these shapes and the point O on to squared paper.

Enlarge the shape by the scale factor given, using O as the centre of enlargement.

a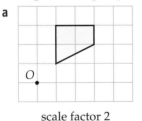

scale factor 2

b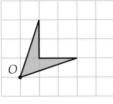

scale factor 3

c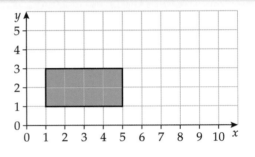

scale factor 4

4 In this diagram, shape B is an enlargement of shape A.

a What is the scale factor of the enlargement?

b What are the coordinates of the centre of enlargement?

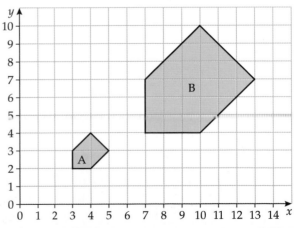

5 In this diagram, shape H is an enlargement of shape G.

   a What is the scale factor of the enlargement?

   b What are the coordinates of the centre of enlargement?

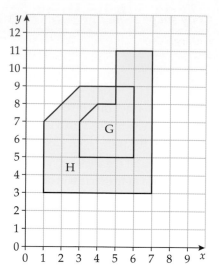

6 On squared paper draw a coordinate grid with x- and y-axes from 0 to 10.

Plot and draw shape A with vertices at $(4, 4)$, $(6, 5)$, $(6, 6)$, $(5, 6)$ and $(4, 5)$.

   a Draw the image of A after an enlargement by scale factor 4 with $(5, 5)$ as the centre of enlargement. Label the image B.

   b What are the coordinates of the vertices of B?

31.2 Enlargements with fractional and negative scale factors

1 The vertices of this shape are at $(4, 2)$, $(4, 8)$, $(6, 4)$, $(8, 8)$ and $(8, 2)$.

   a Enlarge the shape by scale factor $\frac{1}{2}$ using $(0, 0)$ as the centre of enlargement.

   b What are the coordinates of the vertices of the enlargement?

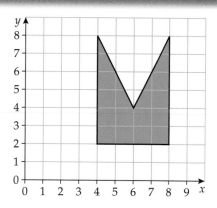

2 A shape has a perimeter of 27 cm. It is enlarged by a scale factor of $\frac{1}{3}$.

What is the perimeter of the enlargement?

3 Copy this shape and the point O on to squared paper.

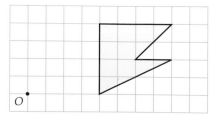

Enlarge the shape by scale factor $\frac{1}{2}$ using O as the centre of enlargement.

4 a Copy shape A and the point O on to squared paper.
  Enlarge the shape by scale factor $\frac{1}{3}$ using O as the centre of enlargement. Label the image B.

b What enlargement will take shape B back to shape A?

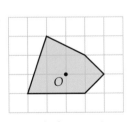

5 In this diagram, triangle P is an enlargement of triangle Q.

a What is the scale factor of the enlargement?

b What are the coordinates of the centre of enlargement?

c What enlargement would take triangle P back to triangle Q?

> Copy the diagram, then draw lines from the vertices of Q to the vertices of P.

6 Copy each of these shapes and the point O on to squared paper.
Enlarge the shape by the scale factor given, using O as the centre of enlargement.

a
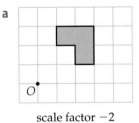

scale factor −2

b
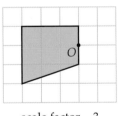

scale factor −3

c

scale factor −2

7 a Copy the diagram onto squared paper.

b Enlarge shape W by a scale factor of $-\frac{1}{2}$ using C as the centre of enlargement. Label the image Z.

c What is the enlargement that will take Z back to W?

Links to:

Higher Student Book
Ch32, pp.475–495

Key Points

Congruency   C   A*

Two objects are congruent if they are identical in shape and size.

Two objects are similar when they are exactly the same shape, but not the same size.

The four conditions for congruence of triangles are

- SSS (side, side, side)
- SAS (side, angle, side)
- ASA (angle, side, angle)
- RHS (right angle, hypotenuse, side).

Similarity   C   B

For two shapes to be similar

- the corresponding angles must be equal
- the ratios of corresponding sides must be the same.

Areas and volumes of similar shapes   A

When a shape is enlarged by a linear scale factor k

enlarged area $= k^2 \times$ original area

enlarged volume $= k^3 \times$ original volume

32.1   Congruency and similarity

C

1   a   Draw one shape that is congruent to this shape.

     b   Draw one shape that is similar to this shape.

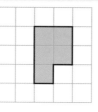

2   Look at the shapes in this diagram.

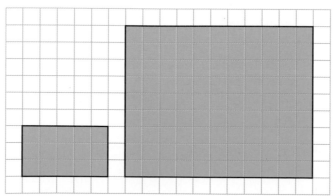

   a   Write down the letters of the shapes that are congruent to A.

   b   Write down the letters of the shapes that are similar to A.

3   Look at these shapes.

Explain why the two rectangles are not similar.

4 Look at the following pairs of triangles.

For each pair state whether or not they are congruent, giving the appropriate reason.

a

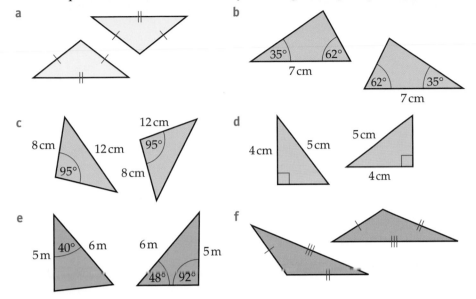

b

c

d

e

f

32.2 Lengths of similar shapes

1 Here are two similar triangles.

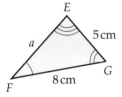 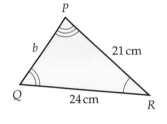

Work out the unknown lengths *a* and *b*.

2 Kite *HIJK* is an enlargement of kite *LMNP*.

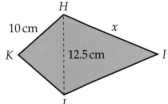

a Work out the unknown lengths *x* and *y*.

b What is the ratio of the perimeters of these kites?

3 Samantha says that these two triangles are similar.

Is she correct? Show workings to support
your answer.

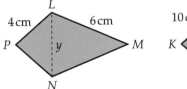

4 Two tins of coffee are similar.

The larger tin is 20 cm high and has a radius of 6 cm.

The smaller tin is 12 cm high.

What is the radius of the smaller tin?

32.3 Areas and volumes of similar objects

A

1 Here are two mathematically similar triangles.

  a Work out the length of the hypotenuse of the large triangle.

  b The area of the small triangle is 54 cm².
    Work out the area of the large triangle.

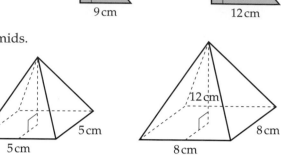

2 Here are two mathematically similar square-based pyramids.

  a The height of the large pyramid is 12 cm.
    Work out the height of the small pyramid.

  b The surface area of the small pyramid is 104 cm².
    Calculate the surface area of the large pyramid.

  c The volume of the large pyramid is 256 cm³.
    Calculate the volume of the small pyramid.

  d The mass of the small pyramid is 281.25 g. Calculate the mass of the large pyramid.

A

3 A party organiser has two sizes of mathematically similar helium balloons.

The larger size has a height of 75 cm and a volume of 80 litres.
The smaller size has a height of 30 cm.

A canister of helium contains 1400 litres. Does the party organiser have enough helium to fill 12 large balloons and 120 small balloons?

AO2

32.4 Congruent triangle proof

A*

1 ABCD is a rhombus.

Prove that triangle ABC is congruent to triangle ADC.

2 ABCDE is a regular pentagon.

Prove that triangle ABC is congruent to triangle EDC.

3 In the diagram the lines AC and BD intersect at E.

AB and DC are parallel.

The length AB is equal to the length CD.

Prove that triangle ABE is congruent to triangle CDE.

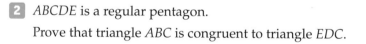
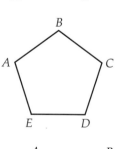
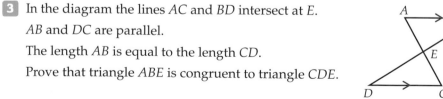

AO3

32 Congruency and similarity

Key Points

Pythagoras' theorem   [C]

For a right-angled triangle with sides of lengths a, b and c, where c is the hypotenuse, Pythagoras' theorem states that $a^2 + b^2 = c^2$.

You can calculate the length of a shorter side of a right-angled triangle using

- $a^2 = c^2 - b^2$
- $b^2 = c^2 - a^2$

Length of a line segment   [C]

Pythagoras' theorem can be used to find the length of a diagonal line, AB, given the coordinates of A and B.

Trigonometry   [B]

Trigonometric functions are used to calculate lengths or angles in right-angled triangles.

The basic trigonometric functions are given by

$$\sin x = \frac{\text{opposite}}{\text{hypotenuse}}$$

$$\cos x = \frac{\text{adjacent}}{\text{hypotenuse}}$$

$$\tan x = \frac{\text{opposite}}{\text{adjacent}}$$

Applications of Pythagoras' theorem and trigonometry   [C] [B] [A] [A*]

For a cone, Pythagoras' theorem connecting r, h and l is $r^2 + h^2 = l^2$.

The longest diagonal (x) in a cuboid with dimensions $a \times b \times c$ is found by applying Pythagoras' theorem to two triangles. $x^2 = a^2 + b^2 + c^2$

Trigonometry and Pythagoras' theorem can be used to find the angle between a line and a plane.

33.1   Pythagoras' theorem

1 Calculate the lengths marked with letters in these triangles. All lengths are in centimetres.   [C]

a
a, 24, 10

b
b, 11, 6.6

c
14.3, 5.5, c

d
d, 0.7, 2.4

e
e, 40, 41

f
240, 250, f

2 A2 paper measures 59.5 cm by 42 cm.   [C]

What is the length of the diagonal of a sheet of A2 paper?

Give your answer to the nearest millimetre.

3 A cuboid is cut through four of its vertices, $ABCD$, leaving two identical pieces. The diagram shows one of the pieces.

Calculate the length of the line AC.
Give your answer correct to one decimal place.

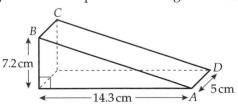

7.2 cm, 14.3 cm, 5 cm

AO3

4 The shortest side of a right-angled triangle is 7 cm.
The triangle is inside a circle of radius 5.2 cm as shown.
Calculate the area of the triangle.
Give your answer correct to one decimal place.

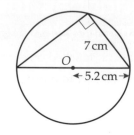

7 cm

O

←5.2 cm→

5 The diagram shows a sketch of part of a pendant that Jamil is making.
The pendant is silver with a fine gold wire around the perimeter and across the diagonal.
Work out the length of gold wire that Jamil needs.
Give your answer correct to the nearest mm.

2 cm

1 cm

1 cm

3 cm

2 cm

3 cm

6 Calculate the length of each of these line segments.
Give your answer correct to one decimal place where appropriate.

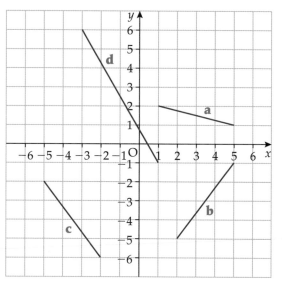

7 Calculate the length of the line segment from $(-1, -3)$ to $(4, 9)$.

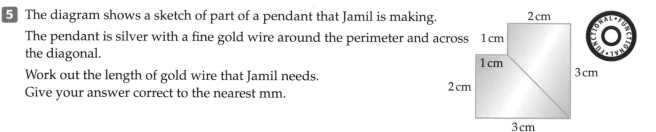

33.2 Trigonometry – the ratios of sine, cosine and tangent

1 Sketch this triangle and label the sides H, O and A. x is the angle to be found.

x

2 Use your calculator to work out the values of the following trigonometric functions.
Give your answers correct to five decimal places.

a $\sin 35°$ b $\cos 35°$ c $\tan 35°$

d $\sin 135°$ e $\cos 135°$ f $\tan 135°$

3 Use your calculator to find the size of each angle. Give your answers correct to one decimal place.

a $\cos x = 0.8818$ b $\sin x = 0.3443$ c $\tan x = 1.9275$

1 Calculate the length, x, marked on each diagram. All lengths are in centimetres.
Give your answers correct to one decimal places where appropriate.

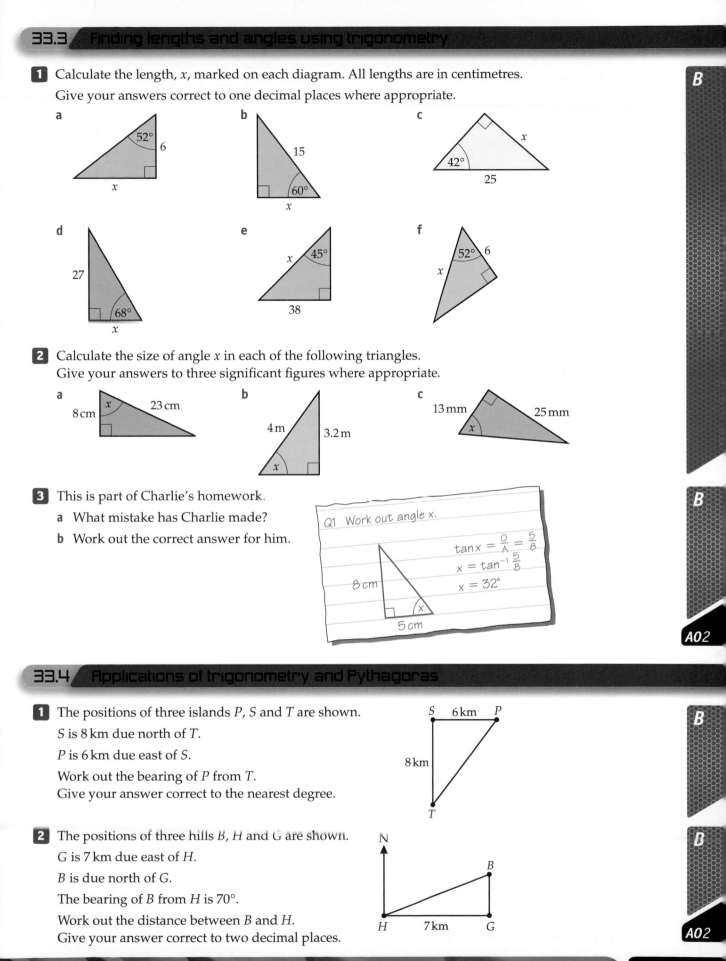

a

52°
6
x

b

15
60°
x

c

x
42°
25

d

27
68°
x

e

x 45°
38

f

52° 6
x

2 Calculate the size of angle x in each of the following triangles.
Give your answers to three significant figures where appropriate.

a
x 23 cm
8 cm

b
4 m   3.2 m
x

c
13 mm   25 mm
x

3 This is part of Charlie's homework.

a What mistake has Charlie made?

b Work out the correct answer for him.

Q1 Work out angle x.

8 cm

x

5 cm

$\tan x = \dfrac{O}{A} = \dfrac{5}{8}$

$x = \tan^{-1} \dfrac{5}{8}$

$x = 32°$

AO2

1 The positions of three islands P, S and T are shown.

S is 8 km due north of T.

P is 6 km due east of S.

Work out the bearing of P from T.
Give your answer correct to the nearest degree.

S 6 km P

8 km

T

2 The positions of three hills B, H and G are shown.

G is 7 km due east of H.

B is due north of G.

The bearing of B from H is 70°.

Work out the distance between B and H.
Give your answer correct to two decimal places.

N

B

H 7 km G

AO2

B

3 A home owner wants to build a driveway from a parking space by a house to the road.
The diagrams show the plan view and the side view of the house and road.

Plan view

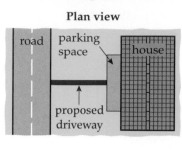

Side view

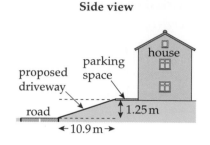

The parking space is 1.25 m above the road.

The parking space is a horizontal distance of 10.9 m from the road.

The maximum safe angle allowed, for a driveway, is 6° from the horizontal.

Can the home owner build a safe driveway in a direct line from the parking space to the road?

4 Calculate the area of this triangle.
Give your answer correct to three significant figures.

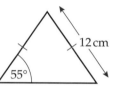

AO3

C

5 A 25 cm long stirring stick is dropped into a partly used tin of paint.
The top of the stick is exactly level with the top of the paint.

The diameter of the paint tin is 24 cm.

How many litres of paint are in the tin?
Give your answer to the nearest litre.

| 1000 cm³ = 1 litre |

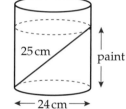

AO2

A

6 The curved surface area of this cone is 180 cm².
The radius of the base of the cone is 6 cm.

The formula for the curved surface area (SA) of a cone is given by
SA = $\pi r l$, where r is the radius and l is the slant height.

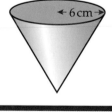

   a Work out the slant height of the cone.

   b Work out the perpendicular height of the cone.

   c Work out the volume of the cone.

| **volume of cone** = $\frac{1}{3}$ × **base area** × **height** |

Give all your answers to three significant figures.

AO2

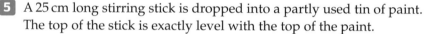

33.5 **Angles of elevation and depression**

B

1 Shannon is 75 m from a tall tree.

The angle of elevation of the top of the tree is 39°.

How tall is the tree? Give your answer to the nearest metre.

2 Kerry is standing on the beach looking out to sea at a wind turbine.

The wind turbine is 7.5 km from the beach.

The angle of elevation of the top of the wind turbine is 0.9°.

AO2 How tall is the wind turbine? Give your answer to the nearest metre.

3 Doug is standing near the foot of a 120 m high cliff.

On the top of the edge of the cliff is a tree.

The angle of elevation to the top of the cliff is 67.4°.

The angle of elevation to the top of the tree is 71°.

Calculate the height of the tree. Give your answer correct to three significant figures.

4 From the top of a 255 m skyscraper the angles of depression of two hot-dog stands are 15° and 19° respectively.

Calculate the distance between the two hot-dog stands assuming that all three buildings are in line and that the ground between them is level. Give your answer to the nearest metre.

33.6 Problems in three dimensions

In this exercise, give all answers correct to three significant figures.

1 The diagram shows a unit cube.

Work out the length of

a *AE*

b *AF*

> In a unit cube, all the lengths of the edges are 1 unit.

2 The diagram shows a cube of side length 2 cm.

Calculate the length *AF*.

3 The diagram shows a cuboid.

AB = 5 cm, *AD* = 10 cm and *DE* = 4 cm.

Calculate the angle between *AF* and the base *ADEH*.

4 A cuboid is cut through four of its vertices, *BGDE*, leaving two identical pieces. The diagram shows one of the pieces.

Calculate the size of the angle between *DG* and the base *ADEH*.

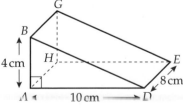

Links to:
Higher Student Book
Ch34, pp.523–537

Key Points

Circle properties

The perpendicular from the centre of a circle to a chord bisects the chord.

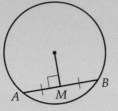

Tangents drawn to a circle from an external point are equal in length.

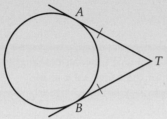

The angle between a tangent and radius is 90°.

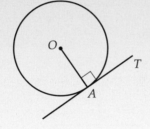

Circle theorems   **B** **A** **A⁺**

The angle subtended by an arc at the centre of a circle is twice the angle that it subtends at the circumference.

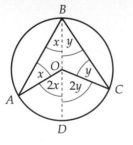

B The angle in a semicircle is a right angle.

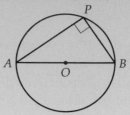

Angles subtended by the same arc are equal.

Opposite angles in a cyclic quadrilateral are supplementary.

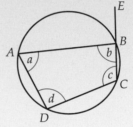

$\angle ABC + \angle CDA = 180°$

The exterior angle of a cyclic quadrilateral is equal to the opposite interior angle.

$\angle CDA = \angle ABE$

The angle between a tangent and a chord is equal to the angle in the alternate segment.

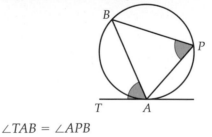

$\angle TAB = \angle APB$

34.1   Tangents and chords

B

1 In the diagram, the length of the chord AB is 10 cm.

The mid-point of the chord is 5 cm from the centre of the circle.

Calculate the length of the radius of the circle. Write your answer correct to three significant figures. Write down any circle properties that you use.

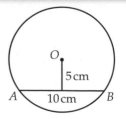

2 In the diagram, the circle with centre O has a radius of 11.1 cm.
The length of the chord AB is 5.3 cm.
Using Pythagoras' theorem, find the length of OM, where M is the mid-point of AB.
Give your answer correct to one decimal place.

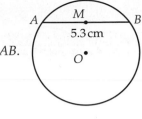

3 Calculate the size of angle x in the diagram.
Write down any circle properties you use.

4 Calculate the size of angle x in the diagram.
Write down any circle properties you use.

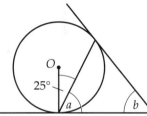

5 Calculate the sizes of angles a and b in the diagram. Explain how you worked
out your answers.

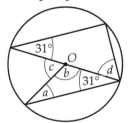

6 OA is the radius of a circle.
BA is a tangent to the circle and has a length of 40 cm. BO = 41 cm.
Calculate the diameter of the circle.

34.2 Circle theorems

1 Calculate the sizes of the angles marked with letters. Explain each step in your reasoning.

a 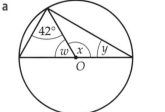 b 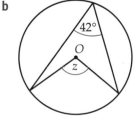 c

2 Calculate the sizes of the angles marked with letters.
Show every step in your working.

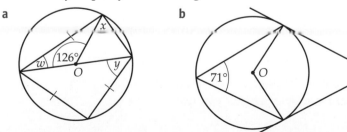

3 Calculate the sizes of the angles marked with letters. Explain each step in your reasoning.

a
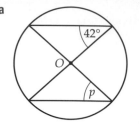

b
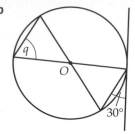

c
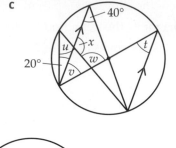

4 *ABCE* is a cyclic quadrilateral.

Lines *AE* and *BC* are extended to meet at *D*.

AC = *CD*

Calculate the size of ∠*ECD*.
Explain each step in your reasoning.

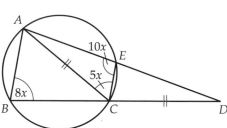

34.3 The alternate segment theorem

1 Calculate the sizes of the angles marked with letters. Explain each step in your reasoning.

a
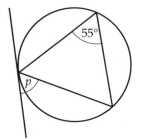

b
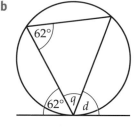

c
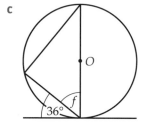

2 Calculate the sizes of the angles marked with letters. Explain each step in your reasoning.

a
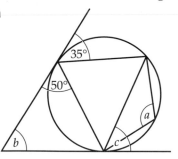

b
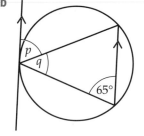

c
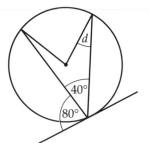

3 *AB* is a tangent to a circle with centre *O*.

PQ are points on the circumference.

Angle *APQ* is *x*°.

a Write down the value of angle *AOQ*.

b Calculate the size of angle *OAQ* in terms of *x*.

c Prove that angle *BAQ* is equal to angle *APQ*.

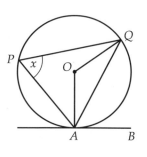

Key Points

Quadratic functions   `D` `C` `B` `A` `A*`

A quadratic function is one in which the highest power of x is x^2. The general form of a quadratic function is given by $y = ax^2 + bx + c$, where a, b and c are constants, with $a \neq 0$.

Quadratic graphs are parabolic (U-shaped) curves that are symmetrical about a line parallel to the y-axis.

Solutions to quadratic equations can be found graphically by finding the points of intersection of the quadratic graph with the x-axis or with other linear graphs.

Cubic functions   `B` `A`

A cubic function is one in which the highest power of x is x^3. The general form of a cubic function is given by $y = ax^3 + bx^2 + cx + d$, where a, b, c and d are constants, with $a \neq 0$.

The solutions of cubic equations of the form $ax^3 + bx^2 + cx + d = 0$ are the values of x where the graph crosses the x-axis.

Reciprocal functions   `A`

A reciprocal function is one in which the power of x is of the form x^{-1} or $\frac{1}{x}$. The general form of a reciprocal function is $y = \frac{a}{x}$, where a is a positive or negative constant.

All reciprocal graphs have two asymptotes. An asymptote is a line that a graph approaches but never touches or crosses.

Combined functions   `A*`

Some functions have reciprocal terms and quadratic, cubic or linear terms. You can draw the graph of a combined function using a table of values.

Exponential functions   `A` `A*`

An exponential function is a function of the form $y = k^x$, where k is a positive number.

All exponential functions of the form $y = k^x$ pass through the point (0, 1).

35.1   Quadratic graphs

1 a Copy and complete the table of values for $y = x^2 - 2$.

x	-3	-2	-1	0	1	2	3
$y = x^2 - 2$	7	2				2	

> Draw a y-axis from -3 to $+15$ and an x-axis from -3 to $+3$. `D`

b Draw the graph of $y = x^2 - 2$ for values of x from -3 to $+3$.

2 a Draw the graph of $y = x^2 + 1$ on the same axes you used in Q1.

b Describe the similarities and differences between the graphs of $y = x^2 + 1$ and $y = x^2 - 2$.

3 a Copy and complete the table of values for $y = x^2 - 2x$.

x	-3	-2	-1	0	1	2	3
x^2	9			0			9
$-2x$	$+6$			0			-6
$y = x^2 - 2x$	15			0			3

b Draw the graph of $y = x^2 - 2x$ on the same axes you used in Q1.

c Describe the similarities and differences between the graphs of $y = x^2 - 2$ and $y = x^2 - 2x$.

4 Use your graphs in Q1 to Q3 to write down the line of symmetry for each of these graphs.

a $y = x^2 - 2$ **b** $y = x^2 + 1$ **c** $y = x^2 - 2x$

5 a Make a table of values, then draw the graph of $y = 3x^2 + 12x - 15$ for values of x from -6 to $+2$.

b Write down the minimum or maximum value of y.

c Write down the line of symmetry of the graph.

d Write down the coordinates of the x-intercept of the line of symmetry.

C

1 **a** Copy and complete the table of values for $y = x^2 + 2x - 2$ for values of x from -3 to $+3$.

x	-3	-2	-1	0	1	2	3
x^2	9				1	4	9
$+2x$	-6				$+2$	$+4$	$+6$
-2	-2				-2	-2	-2
$y = x^2 + 2x - 2$	1				1	6	13

b Draw the graph of $y = x^2 + 2x - 2$ for values of x from -3 to $+3$.

> **Draw a y-axis from -5 to $+15$ and an x-axis from -3 to $+3$.**

c What are the coordinates of the lowest point?

d Write down the line of symmetry.

e What are the coordinates of the points where the curve crosses the x-axis?

f Write down the solutions to the equation $x^2 + 2x - 2 = 0$.

2 **a** Draw the graph of $y = x^2 + x - 6$ for $-4 \leqslant x \leqslant 3$.

b Use your graph to find the solutions to the equation $x^2 + x - 6 = 0$.

C

AO3

3 Using your graph of $y = x^2 + x - 6$ from Q2

a solve the equation $x^2 + x - 6 = -4$

b explain why the equation $x^2 + x - 6 = -7$ cannot be solved.

C

4 **a** Draw the line $y = 2$ on your graph in Q2.

b Write down the coordinates of the points where the line and the curve intersect.

c Write down the quadratic equation whose solutions are the answers to part **b**.

B

5 **a** Copy and complete the table of values for $y = 2x^2 - 2x - 4$ for $-2 \leqslant x \leqslant 3$.

x	-2	-1	0	1	2	3
$2x^2$	8		0			18
$-2x$	$+4$		0			-6
-4	-4		-4			-4
$y = 2x^2 - 2x - 4$	8		-4			8

b Draw the graph of $y = 2x^2 - 2x - 4$ for $-2 \leqslant x \leqslant 3$.

c Draw the line $y = x + 1$ on the graph.

d Write down the coordinates of the points where the line and the curve intersect.

AO2

e Show that the solutions to the equation $2x^2 - 3x - 5 = 0$ can be found at these points.

A*

6 By drawing an appropriate line on your graph in Q5, solve the equation $2x^2 - 4x - 2 = 0$.

AO2

A*

1 A rectangle has dimensions $(x + 5)$ m and $(2x - 3)$ m.

a Show that the area (A) of the rectangle can be written as $A = 2x^2 + 7x - 15$.

AO2

b The area of the rectangle is $45\,\text{m}^2$. Work out the value of x.

A*

2 The length of a rectangle is 6 cm more than its width, w.

The area of the rectangle is $187\,\text{cm}^2$.

AO3

Work out the dimensions of the rectangle.

3 Work out the lengths of the sides of this right-angled triangle.

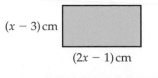

4 Without drawing a graph, work out the points of intersection of the curve $y = x^2 + 2x - 3$ and the straight line $y = 2x + 1$.

5 The areas of the two rectangles shown are equal.

Find the area of one rectangle.

$(x - 3)\,$cm

$(2x - 1)\,$cm

$(x - 2)\,$cm

$(3x - 9)\,$cm

A*

A03

35.4 Graphs of cubic functions

B

1 **a** Copy and complete the table of values for the function $y = x^3 - 4x + 5$.

x	-3	-2	-1	0	1	2	2.5
x^3	-27			0		8	15.6
$-4x$	$+12$			0		-8	-10
$+5$	$\lvert\,5$			$+5$		$+5$	$+5$
$y = x^3 - 4x + 5$	-10			5		5	10.6

b Draw the graph of $y = x^3 - 4x + 5$ for $-3 \leqslant x \leqslant 2.5$.

c Use your graph to find the solution to $x^3 - 4x + 5 = 0$.

2 **a** Draw the graph of $y = x^3 - 2x^2 - x$ for $-2 \leqslant x \leqslant 4$.

b Use your graph to find the solutions to $x^3 - 2x^2 - x = 0$.

3 Without drawing a graph, write down the solutions to $(x - 2)(x - 4)(x + 6) = 0$.

35.5 Graphs of reciprocal functions and combined functions

1 **a** Copy and complete the table of values for the function $y = \dfrac{3}{x}$.

A

x	-3	-2	-1	-0.5	-0.1	0.1	0.5	1	2	3
$y = \dfrac{3}{x}$	-1		-3			30		3		1

b Draw the graph of $y = \dfrac{3}{x}$ for $-3 \leqslant x \leqslant 3$.

2 **a** Draw the graph of $y = \dfrac{3}{x} + 2$ for $-3 \leqslant x \leqslant 3$ on the axes used in Q1.

b Compare and contrast the graphs of $y = \dfrac{3}{x}$ and $y = \dfrac{3}{x} + 2$.

3 **a** Draw the graph of $y = 3 - \dfrac{3}{x}$ for $-3 \leqslant x \leqslant 3$.

b What are the equations of the two asymptotes?

4 **a** Copy and complete the table of values for the function $y = \dfrac{1}{x} + 2x$.

> There's no need to include negative x-values in the table. Why?

x	0.1	0.2	0.5	1	2	3	4	5
$\dfrac{1}{x}$		5			0.5		0.25	0.2
$+2x$		$+0.4$			$+4$		$+8$	$+10$
$y = \dfrac{1}{x} + 2x$		5.4			4.5		8.25	10.2

b Draw the graph of $y = \dfrac{1}{x} + 2x$ for $-5 \leqslant x \leqslant 5$.

5 Draw the graph of $y = x^2 + \dfrac{1}{x} + 2x$ for $-3 \leqslant x \leqslant 3$.

A*

A

1 **a** Copy and complete the table of values for the function $y = \left(\frac{1}{3}\right)^x$.

x	-3	-2	-1	0	1	2	3
$y = \left(\frac{1}{3}\right)^x$	27	9					0.04

b Draw the graph of $y = \left(\frac{1}{3}\right)^x$ for $-3 \leqslant x \leqslant 3$.

c Use your graph to estimate the value of x when $y = 5$.

A*

2 A sample of radioactive material decays according to the exponential function $N = 1000 \times 2^{-\frac{t}{70}}$, where N is the amount of radioactive material in grams and t is the time in seconds.

a Copy and complete the table of values for $0 \leqslant t \leqslant 490$.

b Draw a graph to show the decay of the material over the 490 seconds.

t	0	70	140	210	280	350	490
N		500			62.5		7.8

c Use your graph to estimate the amount of radioactive material remaining after 3 minutes.

d A different radioactive material decays according to the function $N = 1000 \times 2^{-\frac{t}{140}}$.

How does the graph of $N = 1000 \times 2^{-\frac{t}{140}}$ compare with the graph of $N = 1000 \times 2^{-\frac{t}{70}}$?

3 Pollutants can be removed from kerosene by passing it through clay pipes. The amount of pollutants left can be calculated using the exponential formula $P = P_0(0.8)^n$, where P is the amount of pollutants remaining (parts per million, ppm), P_0 is the amount of pollutants before purification (ppm) and n is the time (min) the kerosene spends in the clay pipes.

a Calculate P when $P_0 = 160$ and $n = 12$.

b Use a graph of $P = 160 \times (0.8)^n$ to estimate the length of time taken for the remaining pollutants to
  i drop below 5 ppm   **ii** decrease from 42 ppm to 7 ppm.

A02

C

1 David wants to fence a section of a field for some calves. He is investigating different sizes of rectangular enclosures.

The graph shows how the area of the enclosure shown changes as the value of x varies.

a The enclosed area needs to be greater than 25 m². What is the minimum value of x that David can consider?

b What is the area of the enclosure when $x = \frac{1}{2}$?

c What is the area of the enclosure when $x = 6$?

d Look at your answers to parts **b** and **c**. Which of these values of x would be impossible in real life? Give a reason for your answer.

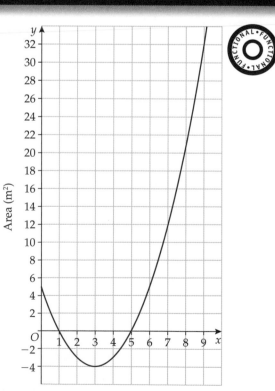

A02

2 Water is poured into each of these containers at the same steady rate.

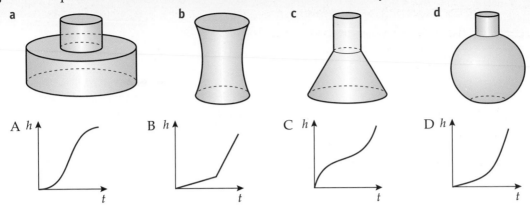

Match each container with the correct graph showing the height, *h*, of the water in the container over time, *t*.

3 Match each of the following functions to the correct graph.

a $y = \dfrac{1}{x}$ **b** $y = x^3 - x^2 - 4x + 4$ **c** $y = -\dfrac{4}{x}$ **d** $y = -x^3$

e $y = -x^2 + 4$ **f** $y = -x$ **g** $y = x^2$ **h** $y = x^2 - 4$

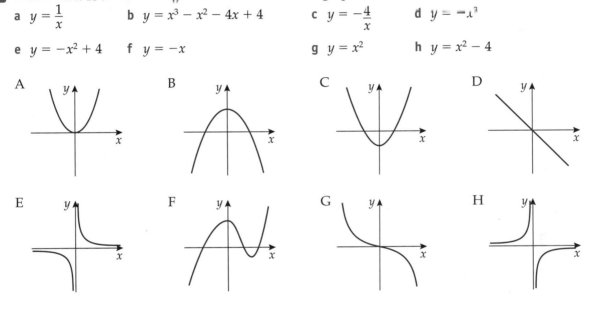

Key Points

Graphs of trigonometric functions | **A**

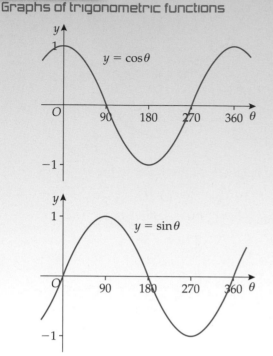

Trigonometric equations | **A***

To solve $\sin x = p$ or $\cos x = q$, where p and q are numbers, get one solution from your calculator and use the symmetry of the curve to find other solutions in the required range.

Calculating areas | **A** **A***

area of a triangle $= \frac{1}{2}ab \sin C$

area of minor segment
$$= \text{area of sector} - \text{area of triangle}$$
$$= \frac{\theta}{360} \times \pi r^2 - \frac{1}{2}r^2 \sin \theta$$

Triangle formulae | **A** **A***

Sine rule
$$\frac{a}{\sin A} = \frac{b}{\sin B} = \frac{c}{\sin C}$$

Cosine rule
$$a^2 = b^2 + c^2 - 2bc \cos A$$
$$\cos A = \frac{b^2 + c^2 - a^2}{2bc}$$

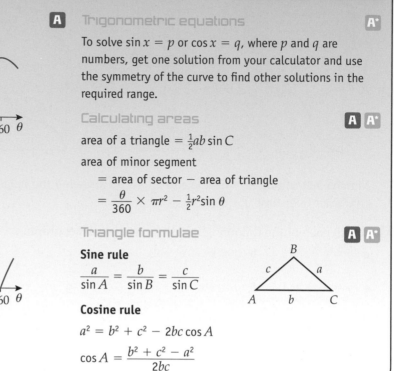

36.1 Graphs of circular functions

A

1 Look at this wheel diagram for $\theta = 60°$.

Sketch your own wheel diagram.
Mark the position of P on the diagram for each of the angles in the table.
Work out whether the trigonometric ratios are positive or negative.
Copy and complete the table.

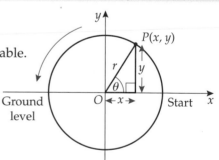

Angle turned through	Positive or negative?		
	$\sin \theta$	$\cos \theta$	$\tan \theta$
60°	+	+	+
100°			
245°			
275°			
−5°			
730°			

2 Write down the missing angles from each of these statements.

All of the missing angles are obtuse angles.

a $\sin 30° = \sin \boxed{}°$

b $\cos 200° = \cos \boxed{}°$

c $\tan 300° = \tan \boxed{}°$

1 For each part, find all the solutions of the equation in the range $0° \leqslant \theta \leqslant 360°$.
Give your answers to the nearest degree.

a $\sin \theta = 0.2$ b $\sin \theta = -0.2$ c $\cos \theta = 0.2$

d $\cos \theta = -0.2$ e $\sin \theta = \dfrac{1}{\sqrt{2}}$ f $\cos \theta = \dfrac{\sqrt{3}}{2}$

A*

2 a Find the two values of a that satisfy the equation $a^2 = 0.49$.

b Sketch the graph of $y = \sin \theta$ for $0° \leqslant \theta \leqslant 360°$.

c Find all the solutions of the equation $(\sin \theta)^2 = 0.49$ in the interval $0° \leqslant \theta \leqslant 360°$.
Give all your answers correct to one decimal place.

1 Calculate the areas of these triangles. Give your answers correct to three significant figures.

A

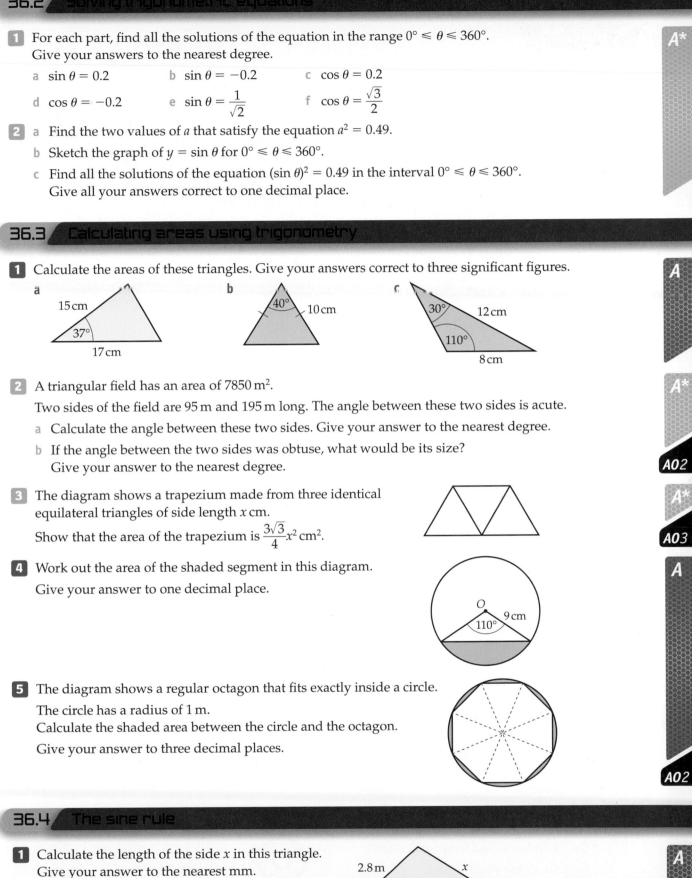

a
15 cm
37°
17 cm

b
40°
10 cm

c
30°
12 cm
110°
8 cm

2 A triangular field has an area of $7850\,\text{m}^2$.

Two sides of the field are 95 m and 195 m long. The angle between these two sides is acute.

a Calculate the angle between these two sides. Give your answer to the nearest degree.

b If the angle between the two sides was obtuse, what would be its size?
Give your answer to the nearest degree.

A*

AO2

3 The diagram shows a trapezium made from three identical
equilateral triangles of side length x cm.

Show that the area of the trapezium is $\dfrac{3\sqrt{3}}{4}x^2\,\text{cm}^2$.

A*

AO3

4 Work out the area of the shaded segment in this diagram.

Give your answer to one decimal place.

O
9 cm
110°

A

5 The diagram shows a regular octagon that fits exactly inside a circle.

The circle has a radius of 1 m.
Calculate the shaded area between the circle and the octagon.

Give your answer to three decimal places.

AO2

1 Calculate the length of the side x in this triangle.
Give your answer to the nearest mm.

A

2.8 m
x
41°
32°

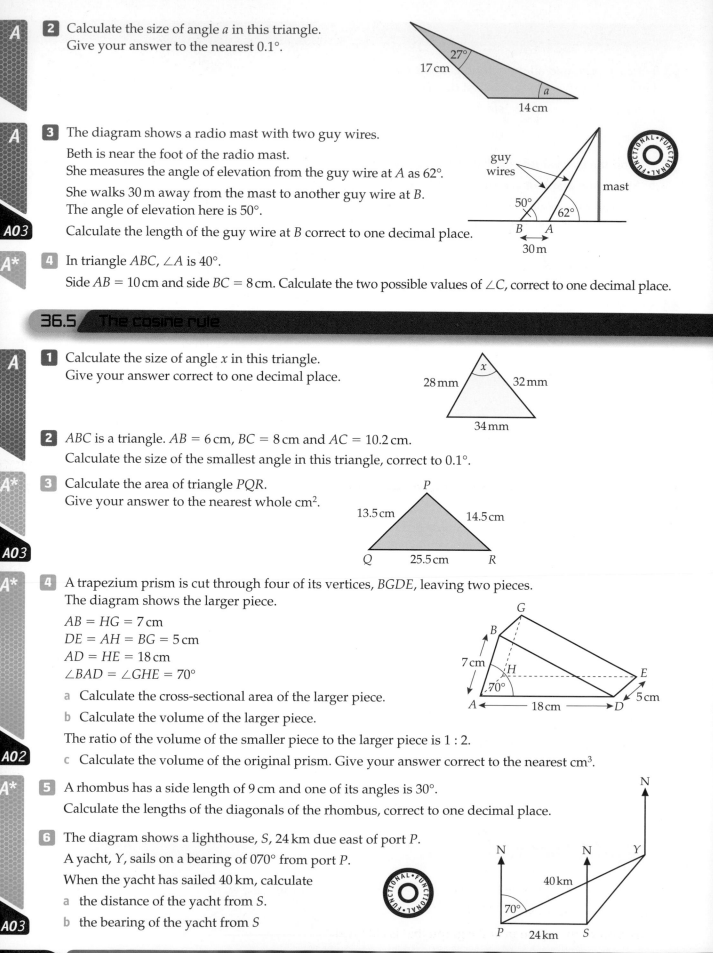

A **2** Calculate the size of angle *a* in this triangle.
Give your answer to the nearest 0.1°.

17 cm
27°
14 cm
a

A **3** The diagram shows a radio mast with two guy wires.

Beth is near the foot of the radio mast.
She measures the angle of elevation from the guy wire at *A* as 62°.

She walks 30 m away from the mast to another guy wire at *B*.
The angle of elevation here is 50°.

AO3 Calculate the length of the guy wire at *B* correct to one decimal place.

guy wires
mast
50°
62°
B *A*
30 m

A* **4** In triangle *ABC*, ∠*A* is 40°.
Side *AB* = 10 cm and side *BC* = 8 cm. Calculate the two possible values of ∠*C*, correct to one decimal place.

36.5 The cosine rule

A **1** Calculate the size of angle *x* in this triangle.
Give your answer correct to one decimal place.

28 mm
x
32 mm
34 mm

2 *ABC* is a triangle. *AB* = 6 cm, *BC* = 8 cm and *AC* = 10.2 cm.
Calculate the size of the smallest angle in this triangle, correct to 0.1°.

A* **3** Calculate the area of triangle *PQR*.
Give your answer to the nearest whole cm².

P
13.5 cm
14.5 cm
Q 25.5 cm *R*

AO3

A* **4** A trapezium prism is cut through four of its vertices, *BGDE*, leaving two pieces.
The diagram shows the larger piece.

AB = *HG* = 7 cm
DE = *AH* = *BG* = 5 cm
AD = *HE* = 18 cm
∠*BAD* = ∠*GHE* = 70°

a Calculate the cross-sectional area of the larger piece.

b Calculate the volume of the larger piece.

The ratio of the volume of the smaller piece to the larger piece is 1 : 2.

AO2 c Calculate the volume of the original prism. Give your answer correct to the nearest cm³.

G
B
7 cm
H
70°
A 18 cm *D*
E
5 cm

A* **5** A rhombus has a side length of 9 cm and one of its angles is 30°.
Calculate the lengths of the diagonals of the rhombus, correct to one decimal place.

6 The diagram shows a lighthouse, *S*, 24 km due east of port *P*.
A yacht, *Y*, sails on a bearing of 070° from port *P*.
When the yacht has sailed 40 km, calculate

a the distance of the yacht from *S*.

AO3 b the bearing of the yacht from *S*

N
N
N
Y
40 km
70°
P 24 km *S*

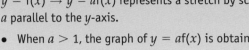

Links to:
Higher Student Book
Ch37, pp.588–600

Key Points

Functions and mappings [B]

An example of a function is $y = x^2$.

In function notation, this would be written as $f(x) = x^2$, where f denotes the function.

$f(x) = x^2$ means the function of x is x^2.

In mapping notation, $y = x^2$ would be written as $f : x \rightarrow x^2$. This is read as, 'the function f maps x to x^2.'

Translations of graphs [A*]

- $y = f(x) \rightarrow y = f(x) + a$
  represents a translation of $\binom{0}{a}$.
- $y = f(x) \rightarrow y = f(x) - a$
  represents a translation of $\binom{0}{-a}$.
- $y = f(x) \rightarrow y = f(x + a)$
  represents a translation of $\binom{-a}{0}$.
- $y = f(x) \rightarrow y = f(x - a)$
  represents a translation of $\binom{a}{0}$.

Stretches of graphs [A*]

$y = f(x) \rightarrow y = af(x)$ represents a stretch by scale factor a parallel to the y-axis.

- When $a > 1$, the graph of $y = af(x)$ is obtained by vertically stretching $y = f(x)$.
- When $0 < a < 1$, the graph of $y = af(x)$ is obtained by vertically shrinking $y = f(x)$.

$y = f(x) \rightarrow y = f(ax)$ represents a stretch from the y-axis, parallel to the x-axis, of scale factor $\frac{1}{a}$.

- When $a > 1$, the graph of $y = f(ax)$ is obtained by horizontally shrinking $y = f(x)$.
- When $0 < a < 1$, the graph of $y = f(ax)$ is obtained by horizontally stretching $y = f(x)$.

37.1 Function notation and mappings

1 Write the following functions using function notation.

   a $y = 5x$ **b** $y = x^2 + 5$ **c** $y = \tan x$ [B]

2 $f(x) = 2x^2 - 2$

   Work out the value of

   a $f(0)$ **b** $f(5)$ **c** $f(-2)$

37.2 Transformations of graphs

1 Sketch the graph of $y = -x$ after a translation of $\binom{5}{0}$.   [A*]

2 Sketch the graph of $y = x^2$ after a translation of $\binom{0}{5}$.

3 Write the equation of the graph obtained when the graph of $y = x^2 - x$ is translated by $\binom{2}{0}$.   [A*]

   [AO2]

4 Describe the transformation that maps the graph of $y = x^2$ onto each of these graphs.   [A*]

   a $y = 5x^2$ **b** $y = 10x^2$ **c** $y = \frac{1}{4}x^2$ **d** $y = (\frac{1}{4}x)^2$

5 Describe the combination of transformations that maps the graph of $y = x^2$ on to the graph of $y = \frac{1}{4}x^2 - 5$.

6 The graph of $y = 2x^2$ is stretched by a scale factor of $\frac{1}{2}$ parallel to the y-axis, followed by a translation of $\binom{0}{-2}$.

   Write down the equation of the graph that is obtained.

A*

1 a Draw a set of axes with x-values from $0°$ to $360°$ and y-values from -4 to $+4$.

b On your axes, sketch the graphs of
  i $y = \sin x$
  ii $y = 3\sin x$
  iii $y = \sin(3x)$
  iv $y = \sin x + 3$

c Describe the transformations that take the graph in part **b i** to the graphs in parts **b ii**, **b iii** and **b iv**.

d State the period and amplitude of each of the graphs in part **b**.

2 a Draw a set of axes with x-values from $0°$ to $360°$ and y-values from -2 to $+2$.

b On your axes, sketch the graphs of
  i $y = \cos x$
  ii $y = 2\cos x$
  iii $y = \cos(2x)$

c Describe the transformations that take the graph in part **b i** to the graphs in parts **b ii** and **b iii**.

d State the period and amplitude of each of the graphs in part **b**.

A*

3 Here is the graph of a function $y = a\sin x + b$.

a What is the value of b?

b What is the value of a?

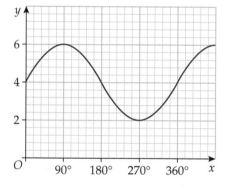

Key Points

Definition, representation and notation for vectors [A]

A vector quantity is one which has magnitude (size) and direction. It can be represented by a line with an arrow on it.

Vectors are equal if they have the same magnitude and direction.

Vectors can be multiplied by scalars (numbers).

Adding and subtracting vectors [A]

In vector addition, $\overrightarrow{AB} + \overrightarrow{BC} = \overrightarrow{AC}$.

$\overrightarrow{AC}$ is called the resultant of vectors $\overrightarrow{AB}$ and $\overrightarrow{BC}$ because going from A to C is the same result as going from A to B and then from B to C.

You can calculate the magnitude and the direction of a vector by using Pythagoras' theorem and trigonometry.

Vector geometry [A*]

The rules for the addition and subtraction of vectors and the multiplication of a vector by a scalar are the key elements in answering questions on vector geometry.

38.1 Definition, representation and notation for vectors

1 Here are three vectors. [A]

$$\mathbf{w} = \begin{pmatrix} 2 \\ 4 \end{pmatrix} \qquad \mathbf{x} = \begin{pmatrix} 3 \\ -2 \end{pmatrix} \qquad \mathbf{y} = \begin{pmatrix} -3 \\ -2 \end{pmatrix}$$

a Draw the following vectors on a square grid.
  i **w**   ii **x**   iii **y**   iv $\frac{1}{2}\mathbf{w}$ v $-\mathbf{x}$ vi $-2\mathbf{y}$

b Write the following as column vectors.
  i 2**w**   ii $-2\mathbf{x}$ iii $-3\mathbf{y}$

38.2 Adding and subtracting vectors

1 Here are three vectors. [A]

$$\mathbf{w} = \begin{pmatrix} 2 \\ 4 \end{pmatrix} \qquad \mathbf{x} = \begin{pmatrix} 3 \\ -2 \end{pmatrix} \qquad \mathbf{y} = \begin{pmatrix} -3 \\ -2 \end{pmatrix}$$

On a square grid, draw diagrams to illustrate these vectors.

a **w** + **x**   b **w** + **y**   c **x** + **y**
d 2**w** + **y**   e **w** − **x** − **y**   f **y** + 2**x** + **w**

2 a Draw a diagram for the vector $\begin{pmatrix} -2 \\ 7 \end{pmatrix}$.

b Find the magnitude and direction of the vector.

> Direction is the angle the vector makes with the positive x-axis.

3 This parallelogram grid shows the vectors $\overrightarrow{AO} = \mathbf{a}$ and $\overrightarrow{OB} = \mathbf{b}$.

Write these in terms of **a** and **b**.

a $\overrightarrow{OW}$ b $\overrightarrow{OD}$ c $\overrightarrow{OZ}$
d $\overrightarrow{OC}$ e $\overrightarrow{UN}$ f $\overrightarrow{WI}$

4 Use the parallelogram grid in Q3 to answer the following.

    a Write down a vector that is equal to $2\mathbf{a} + 2\mathbf{b}$.

    b Write down two other vectors that are equal to $2\mathbf{a} + 2\mathbf{b}$.

    c Write down a vector that is parallel to $\overrightarrow{\lambda O}$.

    d Write down a vector that is half the size of $\overrightarrow{UM}$ and in the opposite direction.

    e Write down, in term of $\mathbf{a}$ and $\mathbf{b}$, the vectors $\overrightarrow{RW}$, $\overrightarrow{FT}$ and $\overrightarrow{K\pi}$.

    Explain the connection between these vectors.

5 This parallelogram grid shows the vectors $\overrightarrow{OA} = \mathbf{a}$ and $\overrightarrow{OB} = \mathbf{b}$.

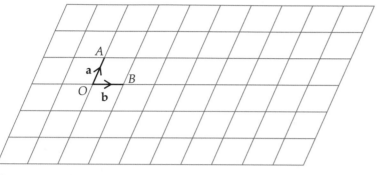

On a copy of the grid, mark the points C to H where

$\overrightarrow{OC} = 3\mathbf{b}$ $\overrightarrow{OD} = -3\mathbf{a}$ $\overrightarrow{OE} = 2\mathbf{a} + 3\mathbf{b}$ $\overrightarrow{OF} = 4\mathbf{b} - \mathbf{a}$ $\overrightarrow{OG} = -2\mathbf{a} - 2\mathbf{b}$ $\overrightarrow{OH} = \frac{5}{2}\mathbf{a} - 2\mathbf{b}$

38.3 Vector geometry

1 ABCDEF is a regular hexagon with centre O.

$\overrightarrow{AB} = \mathbf{a}$ and $\overrightarrow{BC} = \mathbf{b}$.

Find these vectors in terms of $\mathbf{a}$ and $\mathbf{b}$.
Simplify your answers wherever possible.

    a $\overrightarrow{AO}$ **b** $\overrightarrow{AC}$ **c** $\overrightarrow{AD}$ **d** $\overrightarrow{AE}$

    e $\overrightarrow{AF}$ **f** $\overrightarrow{FD}$ **g** $\overrightarrow{EC}$ **h** $\overrightarrow{FB}$

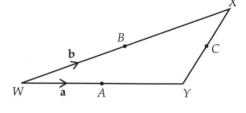

2 The diagram shows the triangle WXY.

A, B and C are the mid-points of WY, WX and XY respectively.

$\overrightarrow{WA} = \mathbf{a}$ and $\overrightarrow{WB} = \mathbf{b}$.

Work out the following vectors in terms of $\mathbf{a}$ and $\mathbf{b}$.
Simplify your answers wherever possible.

    a $\overrightarrow{WX}$ **b** $\overrightarrow{WY}$ **c** $\overrightarrow{AB}$ **d** $\overrightarrow{BA}$

    e $\overrightarrow{YX}$ **f** $\overrightarrow{BY}$ **g** $\overrightarrow{AX}$ **h** $\overrightarrow{WC}$

    i $\overrightarrow{XY}$ **j** $\overrightarrow{BC}$

3 $WXYZ$ is a trapezium with WX parallel to ZY.

$\overrightarrow{ZX} = 3\mathbf{a} + 2\mathbf{b}$

$\overrightarrow{YX} = -\mathbf{a} + 3\mathbf{b}$

    a Work out $\overrightarrow{ZY}$ in terms of $\mathbf{a}$ and $\mathbf{b}$, simplifying your answer as much as possible.

    b $\overrightarrow{ZW} = \mathbf{a} + k\mathbf{b}$, where k is a number yet to be determined.

    Work out $\overrightarrow{WX}$ in terms of $\mathbf{a}$, $\mathbf{b}$ and k and hence work out the value of k.

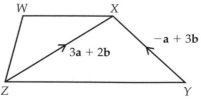

EXAM PRACTICE PAPERS

Unit 1 Higher Statistics and Number

Calculator allowed

1   Indie has these two spinners.

   She spins the spinners at the same time.

   She subtracts the smaller number from the larger
   number to give her a score.

   The table shows her possible scores.

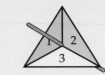

−	1	2	3	4	5
1	0	1	2	3	4
2	1	0	1	2	3
3	2	1	0	1	2

   a   Work out the probability Indie gets a score of 0.   (1 mark) | D
   b   Work out the probability that her score is an odd number.   (2 marks) | D

2   A petrol strimmer costs £92 + $17\frac{1}{2}$% VAT. Work out the total cost of the strimmer.   (2 marks) | D | Funct.

3   These are two 90-day prices plans offered by an electricity supplier.

   Plan A: £0.14 per unit of electricity used

   Plan B: £0.12 per unit of electricity used + £12.70 fixed charge

   In 90 days Mr Vaughan uses, on average, 1200 units of electricity.

   Which plan would it be best for Mr Vaughan to use?

   You must show all your working.   (3 marks) | D | AO3 | Funct.

4   Rohan wants to find out how much exercise people do in a week.

   He has written this question for his survey.

   How much exercise do you do in one week? Please tick one box only.

   2 to 4 hours ☐   *4 to 6 hours* ☐   *6 to 8 hours* ☐

   a   Write down two criticisms of the question.   (2 marks) | D | AO2 | Funct.
   b   Re-write the question to make it more suitable.   (2 marks) | C | AO2 | Funct.

5   An estate agent collects information on the average prices of three-bedroom
   houses at certain distances from a motorway. The table shows his results.

Distance from motorway (km)	2	12	5	3	11	15
Average price (£000s)	164	200	176	172	196	214

   a   Draw a scatter diagram to show this information on a copy of the coordinate
   grid below.   (2 marks) D | Funct.

   [scatter diagram grid: y-axis "Average price (£000s)" from 160 to 220, x-axis "Distance from motorway (km)" from 0 to 16]

   b   The estate agent says that the closer a house is to the motorway, the cheaper it is.

   Do you agree with this statement? Give a reason for your answer.   (1 mark) | D | Funct.

6* The table shows the number of take-away meals eaten each week by a sample of 60 adults.

Number of take-away meals	0	1	2	3	4	5	more than 5
Frequency	16	12	9	8	5	6	4

   a   Is it possible to calculate the mean of this data? Give a reason for your answer.   (2 marks) | D | AO2
   b   Is it possible to calculate the median of this data? Give a reason for your answer. (2 marks) | D | AO2

7   In 2009 the number of people living in a village was 850.

    In 2010 the number of people living in the village was 918.

    A local councillor says

    'If the number of people continues to increase by the same percentage each year, by 2015 there will be more than 1200 people in the village.'

    Do you agree with the local councillor?

    You must show working to support your answer.   **(3 marks)** | C | **AO3** | **Funct.**

8* Nikki and Sara are business partners. Each year they share a £12 000 bonus in the ratio of the number of years they have been in the business.

    This year Nikki has been in the business 6 years and Sara has been in the business 2 years.

    Show that in four years' time the difference between the amounts they receive will be halved.   **(6 marks)** | C | **AO3**

9   The speed of light is approximately 300 million metres per second.

    a   Write this number in standard form.   **(1 mark)** | B

    b   Multiply your answer in part **a** by 60.
        Give your answer in standard form.   **(1 mark)** | B

    c   What do you think your answer to part b represents?   **(1 mark)** | B | **AO2** | **Funct.**

10 This table shows the time taken by 60 adults to complete a puzzle.

Time, t, minutes	Frequency
$0 < t \leqslant 1$	15
$1 < t \leqslant 2$	12
$2 < t \leqslant 3$	23
$3 < t \leqslant 4$	6
$4 < t \leqslant 5$	4

    a   Draw a cumulative frequency diagram to illustrate this information.   **(3 marks)** | B | **AO2**

    b   Use your graph to estimate the median.   **(1 mark)** | B

    c   i   Explain why your answer to part **b** is an estimate.   **(1 mark)** | B | **AO2**

        ii Explain what your answer to part **b** represents.   **(1 mark)** | B | **AO2**

    d   Sue says 'Over 65% of the adults took longer than $2\frac{1}{2}$ minutes to solve the puzzle.'

        Is Sue correct? Explain your answer.   **(2 marks)** | B | **AO2**

11 A survey was carried out at a railway station one week to find out how many trains were late, and by how many minutes (to the nearest minute). This histogram shows the results of the survey.

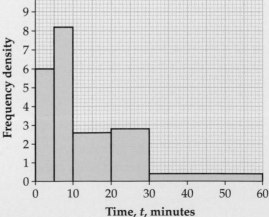

Histogram showing number of late trains and by how many minutes.

    a   What is the total number of trains that were late?   **(3 marks)** | A

    b   How many trains were more than 20 minutes late?   **(1 mark)** | A

    c   Work out an estimate of the mean number of minutes a train is late.   **(3 marks)** | A* | **AO2**

12 The table shows the ages of the members of a tennis club.

Age (years)	Under 15	16–30	31–45	Over 45
Number of members	42	28	16	24

The manager of the tennis club wants a stratified sample of 25 people.

How many members should be chosen from each age group?　　　　**(3 marks)** | A | **Funct.**

13 A science test is in two parts, a written test and a practical test. Out of all the people who sit the written test, 85% pass. When a person passes the written test, the probability that they pass the practical test is 70%. When a person fails the written test, the probability that they fail the practical test is 65%.

What is the probability that a person chosen at random

a fails both tests　　　　**(2 marks)** | A*

b passes exactly one test?　　　　**(3 marks)** | A*

Unit 2 Higher Number and Algebra　　　　Non-calculator

1 The formula to find the area, A, of a rectangle is

$A = l \times w$　　where l is the length and w is the width of the rectangle.

A rectangle has a length of $2x$ cm and a width of $3x - 1$ cm.

a Show that the formula for the area, A, of the rectangle is

$A = 6x^2 - 2x$　　　　**(1 mark)** | D

b Work out the value of A when $x = 6$.　　　　**(2 marks)** | D

2 A two-stage operation is shown.

Input ⟶ | Subtract 5 | ⟶ | Multiply by 2 | ⟶ **Output**

a Work out the output when the input is -3.　　　　**(1 mark)** | D

b When the input is n what is the output?　　　　**(2 marks)** | D

3 The nth term of a sequence is $4n + 5$.

Show that all the terms in the sequence are odd.　　　　**(2 marks)** | D | AO2

4* In the first quarter of the year Melia used 1000 units of electricity.

Each unit of electricity cost 10p

In the second quarter of the year Melia used 10% less units, but each unit cost 10% more.

Will Melia's electricity bill be the same in the second quarter of the year as in the first quarter?

You **must** show your working.　　　　**(4 marks)** | D | AO2 | **Funct.**

5 An electricity supplier uses this formula to work out the total cost of the electricity a customer uses.

$C = 0.1U + 12$　　　　C is the total cost of the electricity in pounds

　　　　　　　　　　U is the number of units of electricity used

a Sam uses 850 units of electricity.

What is the total cost of the electricity she uses?　　　　**(2 marks)** | D | **Funct.**

b The total cost of the electricity Clive used is £84

How many units of electricity did he use?　　　　**(2 marks)** | C | AO2 | **Funct.**

6 Use approximations to estimate the value of

$$\frac{8105}{21.76 \times 0.219}$$　　　　**(3 marks)** | C

7 The surface area of a cube is $(6x + 18)$ cm².

Three of these cubes are used to make the cuboid shown.

The surface area of the cuboid is 98 cm².

Work out the value of x.　　　　**(5 marks)** | C | AO3

8* Steffan works for a company as a sales representative.

At the start of 2009 he bought a car for £20 000.

At the end of 2009 he sold the car for £15 200.

His mileage for the year was 40 000 miles.

The average cost of running his car was 32p per mile.

His company pay him 40p per mile travelled.

What is Steffan's percentage profit or loss after buying, driving and selling the car?

You **must** show your working and clearly state whether Steffan has made a profit or a loss.

(6 marks) | C | AO3 | **Funct.**

9 At a school 60% of the students are girls and 40% are boys.

On one particular day, 10% of the girls and 20% of the boys have the flu.

What percentage of the pupils in the whole school have the flu on this particular day? **(3 marks)** | B | AO2

10 a Solve the equation $4x + 5 = 23 - 2x$ **(3 marks)** | D

b Solve the equation $\dfrac{x + 1}{3} + \dfrac{3x - 5}{2} = 7$ **(4 marks)** | B

11 A is the point $(3, 5)$ and B is the point $(1, -1)$.

Find the equation of the straight line parallel to AB that passes through the point $(4, 2)$.

You must show your working. **(3 marks)** | B | AO3

12 Evan completes a questionnaire.

He ticks this box to show the values his age lies between.

✓ $15 \leqslant a < 20$

a Write down all the whole number ages that Evan could be. **(1 mark)** | D

b Show the inequality $15 \leqslant a < 20$ on a copy of this number line.

12 13 14 15 16 17 18 19 20 21 22

(1 mark) | D

Evan has two brothers, Alun and Berwyn.

The sum of Alun and Berwyn's ages is 44.

The difference is 6.

c Write equations for the sum of their ages and the difference in their ages. **(1 mark)** | B

d Solve the equations simultaneously to find the ages of Alun and Berwyn. **(2 marks)** | B

13 Simplify fully $\dfrac{4x^2 - 25}{2x^2 - x - 15}$ **(5 marks)** | A

14 a Simplify fully $\dfrac{(x^3)^4}{x^2}$ **(2 marks)** | A

b Explain why $125^{-\frac{1}{3}} = \frac{1}{5}$ **(2 marks)** | A* | AO2

15 a Write the expression $x^2 - 4x - 10$ in the form $(x + a)^2 + b$. **(3 marks)** | A*

b Hence, or otherwise, solve $x^2 - 4x - 10 = 0$.

Give your answers in surd form. **(2 marks)** | A*

16 Write the expression $(3 + \sqrt{8})(7 - \sqrt{18})$ in the form $a + b\sqrt{c}$, where a, b and c are integers. **(4 marks)** | A*

Unit 3 Higher Geometry and Algebra — Calculator allowed

1 Work out the area of this shape.

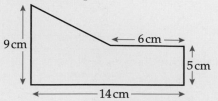

9 cm

6 cm

5 cm

14 cm

Not drawn accurately

(4 marks) | D

2 The diagram shows the position of two lighthouses, P and Q.

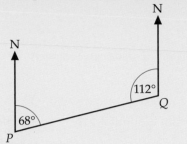

Not drawn accurately

a Explain why the bearing of P from Q is not 112°   **(1 mark)** | **D** | **AO2**

b Work out the bearing of P from Q.   **(2 marks)** | **D**

3 Copy this diagram.

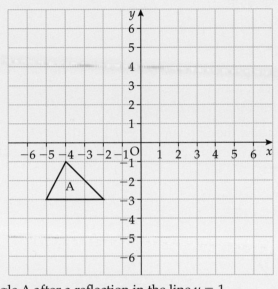

a Draw the image of triangle A after a reflection in the line y = 1.
Label the triangle B.   **(2 marks)** | **D**

b Draw the image of triangle A after a translation by the vector $\binom{6}{4}$.
Label the triangle C.   **(2 marks)** | **C**

4 a When a = 4 and b = 2, work out the value of $2a^2 - 11b$ **(2 marks)** | **D**

b Factorise 12x − 15   **(1 mark)** | **D**

c Write down two possible values of x that would make this statement true.
$x^2 = 16$ **(1 mark)** | **D** | **AO2**

d Ruth compares the cost, per month, of electricity from two different companies.

SW Electricity	N Electric
£0.12 per unit **plus** £24.20 standing charge	£0.15 per unit **plus** £8.60 standing charge

i Write a formula for the total cost, £C, per month for using U units of
electricity with SW Electricity.   **(1 mark)** | **D** | **AO2**

ii Write a formula for the total cost, £T, per month for using U units of
electricity with N Electric.   **(1 mark)** | **D** | **AO2**

iii Ruth uses on average 600 units of electricity per month.
Which electricity company is it cheaper for her to use?
You **must** show your working.   **(3 marks)** | **D** | **AO2** | **Funct.**

iv For how many units of electricity per month would the total cost from
each company be the same?
You **must** show your working.   **(3 marks)** | **D** | **AO2** | **Funct.**

5 An architect has ordered roof trusses to be made for a roof.
This is a sketch of the outline of the roof.

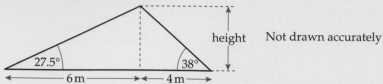

height   Not drawn accurately

27.5°   38°
◄——6 m——►◄—4 m—►

Use a scale drawing to show that the height of the roof is about 3.1 m.   **(3 marks)** | D | AO2 | **Funct.**

6 A solution to the equation $2x^3 - 8x = 162$ lies between 4 and 5.
Use the method of trial and improvement to find this solution correct to 1 decimal place.   **(4 marks)** | C | AO1

7 Calculate the perimeter of a semicircle with diameter 8 cm.
Leave your answer in terms of π.   **(2 marks)** | C | AO2

8 Make a copy of the line RT, exactly 8 cm long.

R ———————————————————— T

Find and shade the region of points that satisfy both of the following conditions.
① The points are nearer to R than T
② The points are not further than 5 cm from T.   **(3 marks)** | C | AO2

9 a On a coordinate grid, draw the graph of $y = x^2 + 2x - 1$ for $-4 \leq x \leq 2$.
Draw the x-axis going from -4 to $+2$ and the y-axis going from -4 to $+10$.   **(3 marks)** | C
b Use your graph to solve the equation $x^2 + 2x - 1 = 1$ **(2 marks)** | C

10* This triangular prism has a total surface area of 152 cm².

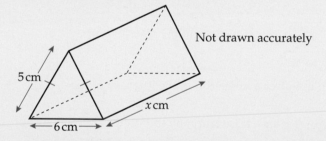

Not drawn accurately

5 cm

x cm

◄—6 cm—►

What is the length, x cm, of the prism?
You **must** show your working.   **(3 marks)** | B | **(2 marks)** | C | AO3

11 a Triangle ABC is right angled at B.
AC = 12 cm and ∠ACB = 42°

A

12 cm   Not drawn accurately

42°   C

B

Show, by calculation that the length of AB is 8.0 cm correct to 1 decimal place.   **(2 marks)** | B | AO2
b Triangle PQR is right angled at Q.
PQ = 25 m and QR = 35 m.
Calculate the size of ∠QPR.

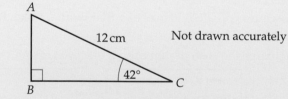

P

25 m   Not drawn accurately

R
35 m   Q

Give your answer correct to 2 significant figures.   **(3 marks)** | B | AO1

12 A building is 40 m tall. It casts a shadow of length 48 m at midday.
A tree next to the building casts a shadow of length 18 m at midday.
Calculate the height of the tree.   **(3 marks)** | B | AO2

13 Mr Smith buys 2 adult and 3 child tickets for a boat trip. He pays a total of £101.50.

Mrs Singh pays £161 for 3 adult tickets and 5 child tickets.

What is the cost of an adult ticket and the cost of a child ticket? **(4 marks) | B | Funct.**

14 The diagram shows a cone.

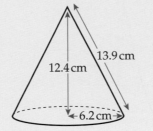

13.9 cm
12.4 cm
6.2 cm

    a Calculate the volume of the cone. **(2 marks) | A | AO1**

    b Calculate the total surface area of the cone. **(3 marks) | A | AO1**

15 Triangle *RST* has *RS* = 25 cm, *RT* = 16 cm and ∠*RST* = 35°.

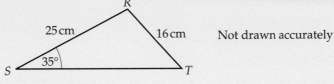

25 cm   16 cm   Not drawn accurately

35°

S   *T*

Calculate the length of *ST*. **(4 marks) | A* | AO2**

16* a   *O* is the centre of the circle.

         EF is a tangent to the circle at *D*.

         Angle *CAD* = 32°.

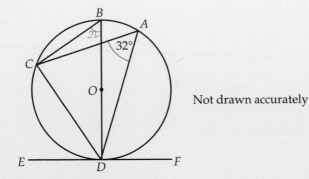

Not drawn accurately

         Work out the size of angle *ODC*.

         You must give reasons for any statements you make. **(2 marks) | A | AO1**

    b   *O* is the centre of the circle.

         PQRS is a cyclic quadrilateral.

         Angle *POR* = 2*x*°.

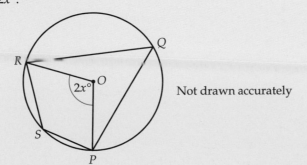

Not drawn accurately

Prove that angle *RQP* + angle *RSP* = 180°. **(3 marks) | A* | AO3**

129

17 This is the graph of $y = x^2 - 2x - 3$.

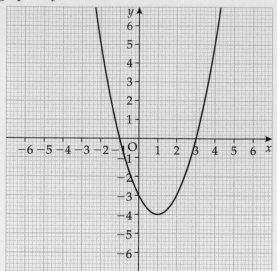

x	-2	-1	0	1	2	3	4
y	5	0	-3	-4	-3	0	5

Use the table of coordinates to make a copy of the graph above.

By drawing an appropriate linear graph, solve the equation $x^2 - 3x - 5 = 0$ **(4 marks)** | A*

18 The diagram shows a cuboid with a square cross section.

The length of the cuboid is twice the height.

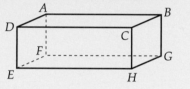   Not drawn accurately

Calculate the angle between *BE* and the base *EFGH*.   **(5 marks)** | A* | AO3

1* **a** There are 50 members in a scuba diving club.

22 of the members are women.

What percentage of the members are men?　　　　　　**(3 marks)** | D

b The rate of VAT was raised in January 2010 from 15% to $17\frac{1}{2}$%.

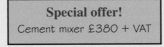

> **Special offer!**
> Cement mixer £380 + VAT

Work out the difference in price of a cement mixer due to the increase in VAT.

(3 marks) | D | AO2 | Funct.

2 Enid is travelling to Cumbria for her holiday.

She begins her journey at 9 am and travels 80 km in the first hour.

Between 10 am and 11 am she travels only 50 km due to heavy traffic.

At 11 am she stops for a half-hour break.

She reaches her destination after a further $2\frac{1}{2}$ hours and a distance of 150 km.

a Draw a distance–time graph of Enid's journey.　　　　**(4 marks)** | D | AO2

b During which section of her journey was Enid travelling the fastest?

Explain how you know.　　　　　　　　　　**(1 mark)** | D

c Work out Enid's average speed for the whole journey.　**(3 marks)** | D | Funct.

3 A shoe shop records the number of each size shoe it sells.
These are the results for one week.

Shoe size	Frequency
4	1
5	14
6	17
7	0
8	8

a Write down the range of this data.　　　　　　　**(1 mark)** | D

b Write down the mode of this data.　　　　　　　**(1 mark)** | D

c Calculate the mean shoe size sold.　　　　　　　**(3 marks)** | D

4 Here is a trapezium.

9.7 cm

x

12 cm

65°

15.3 cm

a State the value of x.　　　　　　　　　　　**(1 mark)** | D

b Work out the area of the trapezium.　　　　　　**(2 marks)** | D

5* John is a builder. He mixes his own concrete out of sand and cement.

The table shows the sand : cement ratios for different types of concrete.

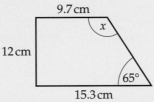

Type of concrete	Sand : cement
general building (above ground)	5 : 1
general building (below ground)	3 : 1
internal walls	8 : 1

John is starting a new job. He estimates that he needs 240 kg of concrete for general building above ground and 180 kg of concrete for internal walls.

Sand and cement are both sold in 25 kg bags.

Work out how many bags of sand and how many bags of cement John needs to buy.

(6 marks) | C | AO2 | Funct.

6 The table shows the distances, d km, that some people cycle to work.

Distance, d (km)	Frequency
$0 \leqslant d < 5$	13
$5 \leqslant d < 10$	9
$10 \leqslant d < 15$	5
$15 \leqslant d < 20$	2
$20 \leqslant d < 25$	3

   a Which class interval contains the median?

      Explain how you worked out your answer.   **(2 marks)** | **C**

   b Explain why it is not possible to calculate the exact mean distance.   **(1 mark)** | **C** | **AO2**

7 Dylan starts with this shape.   He transforms the shape to make this pattern.

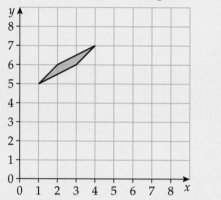 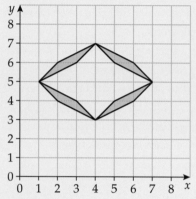

Describe the transformations he uses.   **(4 marks)** | **C** | **AO3**

8* The diagram shows a solid. The lengths x, y and z are shown.

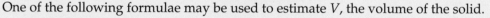

   One of the following formulae may be used to estimate V, the volume of the solid.

$$V = 4x + 2y + 3z$$
$$V = 4x^2y + 2x^2z$$
$$V = 2x(3y^2 + 4z)$$

   a Explain why the formula $V = 4x + 2y + 3z$ cannot be used to estimate the
      volume of the solid.   **(1 mark)** | **B**

   b State, with a reason, which of the above formulae may be used to estimate
      the volume of the solid.   **(2 marks)** | **B**

9* a Factorise $x^2 - 49$ **(2 marks)** | **B**

   b **i** Show that $(x + y)^2 - (x - y)^2 \equiv 4xy$ **(2 marks)** | **B** | **AO2**

      ii Use the identity in part **i** to work out $23^2 - 17^2$ **(2 marks)** | **B** | **AO2**

   c Prove that the sum of three consecutive integers is a multiple of 3.   **(3 marks)** | **B** | **AO3**

10 A report into use of plastic bags in the UK states that approximately 7 800 million
    plastic bags are used in the UK each year.

   a Write this number in standard form.   **(1 mark)** | **B**

   b The population of the UK is approximately 6×10^7.

      What is the mean number of plastic bags used per person in the UK?   **(2 marks)** | **B** | **Funct.**

11 *AC* is a tangent to the circle at *B*.
Angle *EOD* = 210°
Angle *EDB* = 48°.

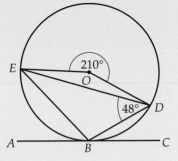

    a Give a reason why angle *EBD* = 105°.   **(1 mark)** | A

    b Work out the value of angle *DBC*.   **(2 marks)** | A

12 The diagram shows a major segment of a circle of radius 15 cm.
The length of the major arc is 27π cm.

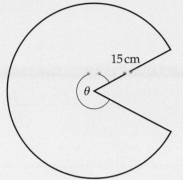

    Calculate the angle of the major segment, marked θ on the diagram.   **(3 marks)** | A

13 A is the point (3, −2) and B is the point (6, 10).
    Work out the equation of the line parallel to AB that passes through the point (1, 9).   **(4 marks)** | A | AO3

14 Simplify $64^{-\frac{2}{3}}$ **(3 marks)** | A*

15 **a** Write the expression $x^2 - 6x - 23$ in the form $(x + p)^2 + q$.   **(2 marks)** | A*

    b Hence solve the equation $x^2 - 6x - 23 = 0$.
        Give your answer in the form $a \pm b\sqrt{2}$.   **(3 marks)** | A*

16 A bag contains three white and four red discs.
Anil takes a disc at random from the bag. He does not replace it.
Bern then takes a disc at random from the bag.
Anil wins if both the discs are the same colour.
Who has a better chance of winning?
You must show working to support your answer.   **(3 marks)** | A* | AO3

Linear Paper 2 Higher tier   **Calculator allowed**

1 Andy and Bari share £240 in the ratio 1 : 3.
How much does Bari get?   **(3 marks)** | D

2 Steven goes shopping. He has £80 to spend.
He spends £24.50 on a pair of squash shoes and £6.99 on some squash balls.
He sees this advert for a squash racket.

> **Squash Racket:** normal price £95
> **Special offer!**
> 45% off normal price

Does Steven have enough money to buy the squash racket?
You **must** show your working.   **(4 marks)** | D | AO2 | Funct.

3 a Use your calculator to work out $\sqrt[3]{117}$.

    i Write down your full calculator display.   **(1 mark)** | D

    ii Write down your answer correct to one decimal place.   **(1 mark)** | D

  b Use your calculator to work out $\dfrac{9.49}{1.88 + 2.27}$

    i Write down your full calculator display.   **(1 mark)** | D

    ii Write down your answer to a suitable degree of accuracy.   **(1 mark)** | D

4 This is the area of a garden that is going to have turf laid to make a new lawn.

Turf costs £2.25 per square metre.

It can only be bought in whole numbers of square metres.

Work out the cost of the turf for the new lawn.

You **must** show your working.

                                                 (4 marks) | D | AO2 | **Funct.**

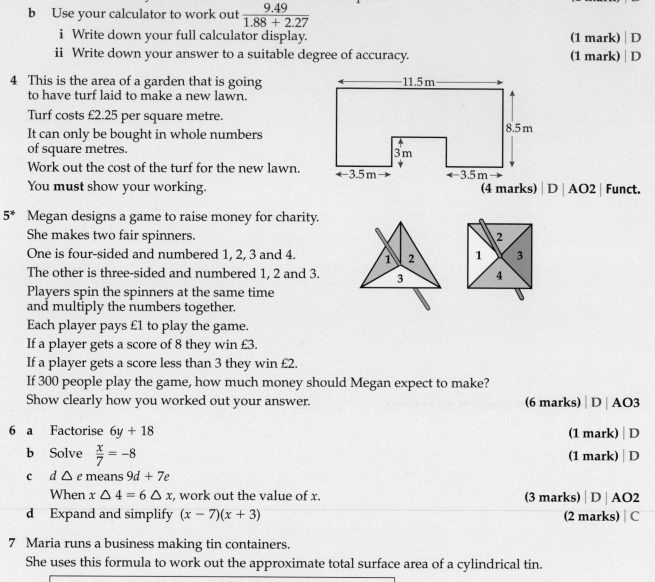

5* Megan designs a game to raise money for charity.

She makes two fair spinners.

One is four-sided and numbered 1, 2, 3 and 4.

The other is three-sided and numbered 1, 2 and 3.

Players spin the spinners at the same time and multiply the numbers together.

Each player pays £1 to play the game.

If a player gets a score of 8 they win £3.

If a player gets a score less than 3 they win £2.

If 300 people play the game, how much money should Megan expect to make?

Show clearly how you worked out your answer.   **(6 marks)** | D | AO3

6 a Factorise $6y + 18$ **(1 mark)** | D

  b Solve $\dfrac{x}{7} = -8$ **(1 mark)** | D

  c $d \triangle e$ means $9d + 7e$

When $x \triangle 4 = 6 \triangle x$, work out the value of x.   **(3 marks)** | D | AO2

  d Expand and simplify $(x - 7)(x + 3)$ **(2 marks)** | C

7 Maria runs a business making tin containers.

She uses this formula to work out the approximate total surface area of a cylindrical tin.

> $A = 6r(r + h)$ where: A is the total surface area in cm^2
> r is the radius of the tin in cm
> h is the height of the tin in cm

  a Use the formula to work out the approximate total surface area of a cylindrical tin with radius 3 cm and height 9 cm.   **(2 marks)** | D | **Funct.**

  b Rearrange the formula to make h the subject.   **(2 marks)** | B | **Funct.**

8 ABCD is a quadrilateral.

Angle D is 90°

Angle $A = x$, angle $B = 3x - 20°$ and angle $C = 2x + 32°$

Work out the largest angle in the quadrilateral.

You **must** show your working.

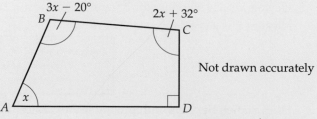

Not drawn accurately

                                                 (5 marks) | D | AO3

9 Harry is going to carry out a survey on visits to the dentist.

These are two of the questions he has written.

> 1. Do you agree that it takes to long to get am appointment to see the dentist?
>
>   Strongly agree ☐   Agree ☐   Don't know ☐
>
> 2. How often do you visit the dentist?

a Give two reasons why question 1 is unsuitable. **(2 marks)** | C

b Give a suitable response section for question 2. **(1 mark)** | C

c Harry decides to carry out his survey outside his local dentist surgery.

Explain why this sample is likely to be unrepresentative. **(1 mark)** | C | AO2

10 a Complete the table of values for $y = x^2 - 2x - 4$. **(2 marks)** | C

x	-3	-2	-1	0	1	2	3	4
y		4	-1	-4		-4	-1	

b Draw a coordinate grid that goes from -3 to $+4$ on the x-axis and -5 to $+15$ on the y-axis.

On the grid, draw the graph of $y = x^2 - 2x - 4$ for values of x from -3 to $+4$. **(2 marks)** | C

c Use your graph to write down the solutions to the equation $x^2 - 2x - 4 = 0$ **(2 marks)** | C

11 M is the point $(5, 6)$ and N is the point $(9, 14)$.

a Work out the midpoint of the line MN. **(2 marks)** | C

b Calculate the length of the line MN.

Give your answer correct to one decimal place. **(2 marks)** | C | AO2

12* a Show that $4(4y - 7) - 5(2y - 9) \equiv 3(2y + 7) - 4$ **(4 marks)** | C | AO3

b Solve the equation $\dfrac{3x + 4}{2} - \dfrac{2x + 1}{3} = 5$ **(4 marks)** | B

13* A company produce two types of light bulb, type A and type B.

The lifetime, in hours, of a sample of 80 of each type of bulb was measured.

The cumulative frequency diagram shows the results for the type A light bulb.

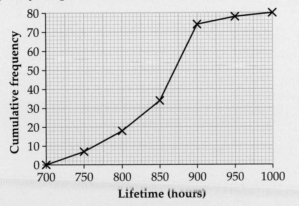

a Estimate the median and interquartile range for the type A light bulb. **(3 marks)** | B | Funct.

b The median and interquartile range for the type B light bulb are 825 hours and 110 hours respectively.

Which type of bulb is longer lasting?

Use the medians and inter-quartile ranges to clearly explain your answer. **(2 marks)** | B | AO2 | Funct.

14 A catering company cooks meals for parties.

They offer three main courses: lasagne (L), fish (F) or quiche (Q).

To accompany the main course they offer either salad (S) or chips (C).

The company use previous data to estimate the number of different types of meals they need to cook. The probability of a person choosing lasagne is 0.4 and fish is 0.5.

The probability of a person choosing salad is 0.25.

a Copy and complete the tree diagram to show all the possible outcomes.

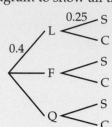

(2 marks) | B | AO2 | Funct.

b Work out the probability that a person chooses fish and chips.

(2 marks) | B | Funct.

c At the next party, 200 guests are expected.

Estimate the number of quiche and salad meals the company will need to cook.

(2 marks) | B | AO2 | Funct.

15 The diagram shows some angles around a point.

a Show that x satisfies the equation $2x^2 + 9x - 200 = 0$

(2 marks) | B | AO2

b Solve the equation $2x^2 + 9x - 200 = 0$.

Hence work out the sizes of the angles around the point.

(4 marks) | A

16 Serge wants to replace the old tiles on his garage roof with new clay tiles.

The recommended minimum angle of elevation of a roof suitable for clay tiles is 35°.

The diagram shows the dimensions of his roof.

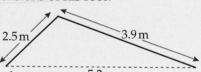

Should Serge use clay tiles on his garage roof?

You **must** show working to support your answer.

(3 marks) | A | AO2 | Funct.

17 A football club has 28 000 season ticket holders.

They are classified by age as follows.

Age (years)	Under 21	21–40	41–60	Over 60
Number of season ticket holders	6440	12 680	7250	1630

The football club wants to take a stratified sample of 500 season ticket holders.

Calculate the number that should be sampled from each age group.

(3 marks) | A | Funct.

18 Two cones are mathematically similar.

The smaller cone has a volume of 120 cm³.

The larger cone has a volume of 405 cm³.

The curved surface area of the smaller cone is 102 cm².

Work out the curved surface area of the smaller cone.

(4 marks) | A | AO3

19 Will draws a circle at two of the opposite vertices of a rhombus.

The rhombus has a side length of 6 cm.

The diagram shows the shape Will has drawn.

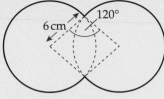

    a Show that the perimeter of the shape is 20π cm.   **(3 marks)** | A | AO2

    b Work out the area of the shape.   **(5 marks)** | A* | AO3

20 OAB is a triangle with $\overrightarrow{OA} = \mathbf{a}$ and $\overrightarrow{OB} = \mathbf{b}$.

M is the mid-point of OB and P is the point on AB such that $AP:PB = 1:2$.

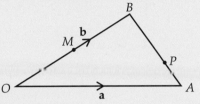

Find expressions for these vectors, in terms of $\mathbf{a}$ and $\mathbf{b}$, simplifying your answers when possible.

    a $\overrightarrow{AB}$ **(1 mark)** | A

    b $\overrightarrow{OM}$ **(1 mark)** | A

    c $\overrightarrow{OP}$ **(2 marks)** | A*

    d $\overrightarrow{MP}$ **(2 marks)** | A*

21 Solve these simultaneous equations using an algebraic method.

$$y - 5x = 2$$
$$y = x^2 + x - 10$$

                                                               (5 marks) | A*